C000098685

Load Lines

International Convention on Load Lines, 1966
and Protocol of 1988, as amended in 2003

CONSOLIDATED EDITION, 2005

INTERNATIONAL
MARITIME
ORGANIZATION

London, 2005

First published in 1981
by the INTERNATIONAL MARITIME ORGANIZATION
4 Albert Embankment, London SE1 7SR
www.imo.org

Third edition 2005

Printed and bound by CPI Group (UK) Ltd, Croydon, CR0 4YY

PEFC/06-37-03

ISBN 978-92-801-4194-8

IMO PUBLICATION
Sales number: IB701E

This publication has been prepared from official documents of IMO, and every effort has been made to eliminate errors and reproduce the original text(s) faithfully. Readers should be aware that, in case of inconsistency, the official IMO text will prevail.

022909

Foreword

Introduction

1   The International Convention on Load Lines, 1966 (1966 LL Convention) was adopted by the International Conference on Load Lines on 5 April 1966 and entered into force on 21 July 1968. It has since been amended by means of Assembly resolutions as follows:

> **.1**   by Assembly resolution A.231(VII), which was adopted on 12 October 1971;
>
> **.2**   by Assembly resolution A.319(IX), which was adopted on 12 November 1975;
>
> **.3**   by Assembly resolution A.411(XI), which was adopted on 15 November 1979;
>
> **.4**   by Assembly resolution A.513(13), which was adopted on 17 November 1983; and
>
> **.5**   by Assembly resolution A.784(19), which was adopted on 23 November 1995.

As far as the 1966 LL Convention is concerned, these amendments had not entered into force at the time of publication of the present consolidated edition.

2   The 1966 LL Convention was modified by the 1988 Protocol relating thereto, which was adopted on 11 November 1988 by the International Conference on the Harmonized System of Survey and Certification and entered into force on 3 February 2000. The intention of the 1988 Protocol is to harmonize the Convention's survey and certification requirements with those contained in SOLAS and MARPOL. The 1988 LL Protocol itself has been modified by the 2003 Amendments, which were adopted by resolution MSC.143(77) on 5 June 2003 and entered into force on 1 January 2005, and by the 2004 Amendments, which were adopted by resolution MSC.172(79) on 9 December 2004 and are expected to enter into force on 1 July 2006. The 1971, 1975, 1979, 1983 and 1995 amendments to the 1966 LL Convention referred to in paragraphs 1.1 to 1.5 above were incorporated into the 1988 LL Protocol, as amended by resolution MSC.143(77).

Content of the consolidated text

3   This publication contains the 1966 LL Convention; the articles of the 1988 LL Protocol; a consolidated text of the 1966 LL Convention as modified by the 1988 LL Protocol, which has been amended by resolution MSC.143(77); the 2004 Amendments to the 1988 LL Protocol, which have not yet entered into force; and the unified interpretations of the 1966 LL Convention approved by the Maritime Safety Committee up to December 2004.

4   The publication has been arranged in six parts:

.1   part 1, which contains a reproduction of the original text of the 1966 LL Convention;

.2   part 2, which contains the Articles of the 1988 LL Protocol;

.3   part 3, containing the 1966 LL Convention as modified by the 1988 LL Protocol, which has been amended by resolution MSC.143(77);

.4   part 4, which contains the 2004 amendments to the 1988 LL Protocol, which were adopted by resolution MSC.172(79) and are expected to enter into force on 1 July 2006;

.5   part 5, which contains the unified interpretations of the 1966 LL Convention approved by the Maritime Safety Committee up to December 2004. These interpretations were originally disseminated by circulars LL.3/Circ. 69, LL.3/Circ. 77, LL.3/Circ. 130 and LL.3/Circ.155; and

.6   part 6, consisting of the Form of Record of conditions of assignment of load lines accepted by the Maritime Safety Committee.

5   In Part 3, those articles and regulations of the 1966 LL Convention which have been modified by the 1988 Protocol, as amended, are indicated by the symbol P88 . It should be noted that, from the legal point of view, the 1988 Protocol is only applicable to ships entitled to fly the flag of a State which is a Party to the Protocol.

6   In accordance with resolution A.351(IX), whereby the Assembly resolved that metric units in the "Système international d'unités" (SI System) should be introduced in the 1974 SOLAS Convention at the first opportunity and also in all future instruments to be adopted under the auspices of the Organization, the text of the 1966 LL Convention as modified by the 1988 Protocol contained in the present publication shows values and dimensions in SI units only. Thus, the values and dimensions in imperial units are omitted only for the purposes of the present publication and also for consistency with the regulations of the Convention that have been modified by the 1988 Protocol, where all dimensions are given in SI units only.

Contents

Part 4
Amendments to the 1988 Protocol that have not yet been accepted by sufficient parties to be able to come into force

Part 5
Unified interpretations of the provisions of the

Part 6
Form of record of conditions of assignment of load lines

Part 1
International Convention
on Load Lines, 1966

INTERNATIONAL CONVENTION ON LOAD LINES, 1966

The Contracting Governments,

DESIRING to establish uniform principles and rules with respect to the limits to which ships on international voyages may be loaded having regard to the need for safeguarding life and property at sea;

CONSIDERING that this end may best be achieved by conclusion of a Convention;

HAVE AGREED as follows:

Article 1
General obligation under the Convention

(1) The Contracting Governments undertake to give effect to the provisions of the present Convention and the annexes hereto, which shall constitute an integral part of the present Convention. Every reference to the present Convention constitutes at the same time a reference to the annexes.

(2) The Contracting Governments shall undertake all measures which may be necessary to give effect to the present Convention.

Article 2
Definitions

For the purpose of the present Convention, unless expressly provided otherwise:

(1) *Regulations* means the regulations annexed to the present Convention.

(2) *Administration* means the Government of the State whose flag the ship is flying.

(3) *Approved* means approved by the Administration.

(4) *International voyage* means a sea voyage from a country to which the present Convention applies to a port outside such country, or conversely. For this purpose, every territory for the international relations of which a Contracting Government is responsible or for which the United Nations are the administering authority is regarded as a separate country.

(5) A *fishing vessel* is a ship used for catching fish, whales, seals, walrus or other living resources of the sea.

(6) *New ship* means a ship the keel of which is laid, or which is at a similar stage of construction, on or after the date of coming into force of the present Convention for each Contracting Government.

3

(7) *Existing ship* means a ship which is not a new ship.

(8) *Length* means 96% of the total length on a waterline at 85% of the least moulded depth measured from the top of the keel, or the length from the fore side of the stem to the axis of the rudder stock on that waterline, if that be greater. In ships designed with a rake of keel the waterline on which this length is measured shall be parallel to the designed waterline.

see also the unified interpretation

Article 3
General provisions

(1) No ship to which the present Convention applies shall proceed to sea on an international voyage after the date on which the present Convention comes into force unless it has been surveyed, marked and provided with an International Load Line Certificate (1966) or, where appropriate, an International Load Line Exemption Certificate in accordance with the provisions of the present Convention.

(2) Nothing in this Convention shall prevent an Administration from assigning a greater freeboard than the minimum freeboard determined in accordance with annex I.

Article 4
Application

(1) The present Convention shall apply to:

(a) ships registered in countries the Governments of which are Contracting Governments;

(b) ships registered in territories to which the present Convention is extended under article 32; and

(c) unregistered ships flying the flag of a State, the Government of which is a Contracting Government.

(2) The present Convention shall apply to ships engaged on international voyages.

(3) The regulations contained in annex I are specifically applicable to new ships.

(4) Existing ships which do not fully comply with the requirements of the regulations contained in annex I or any part thereof shall meet at least such lesser related requirements as the Administration applied to ships on international voyages prior to the coming into force of the present Convention; in no case shall such ships be required to increase their freeboards. In order to take advantage of any reduction in freeboard from that previously assigned, existing ships shall comply with all the requirements of the present Convention.

see also the unified interpretation

(5)   The regulations contained in annex II are applicable to new and existing ships to which the present Convention applies.

Article 5
Exceptions

(1)   The present Convention shall not apply to:

(a) ships of war;

(b) new ships of less than 24 metres (79 feet) in length;

(c) existing ships of less than 150 tons gross;

(d) pleasure yachts not engaged in trade;

(e) fishing vessels.

(2)   Nothing herein shall apply to ships solely navigating:

(a) the Great Lakes of North America and the River St. Lawrence as far east as a rhumb line drawn from Cap des Rosiers to West Point, Anticosti Island, and, on the north side of Anticosti Island, the meridian of longitude 63° W;

(b) the Caspian Sea;

(c) the Plate, Parana and Uruguay Rivers as far east as a rhumb line drawn between Punta Norte, Argentina, and Punta del Este, Uruguay.

Article 6
Exemptions

(1)   Ships when engaged on international voyages between the near neighbouring ports of two or more States may be exempted by the Administration from the provisions of the present Convention, so long as they shall remain engaged on such voyages, if the Governments of the States in which such ports are situated shall be satisfied that the sheltered nature or conditions of such voyages between such ports make it unreasonable or impracticable to apply the provisions of the present Convention to ships engaged on such voyages.

(2)   The Administration may exempt any ship which embodies features of a novel kind from any of the provisions of this Convention the application of which might seriously impede research into the development of such features and their incorporation in ships engaged on international voyages. Any such ship shall, however, comply with safety requirements which, in the opinion of that Administration, are adequate for the service for which it is intended and are such as to ensure the overall safety of the ship and which are acceptable to the Governments of the States to be visited by the ship.

(3)   The Administration which allows any exemption under paragraphs (1) and (2) of this article shall communicate to the Inter-Governmental Maritime

Consultative Organization* (hereinafter called "the Organization") particulars of the same and reasons therefor which the Organization shall circulate to the Contracting Governments for their information.

(4) A ship which is not normally engaged on international voyages but which, in exceptional circumstances, is required to undertake a single international voyage may be exempted by the Administration from any of the requirements of the present Convention, provided that it complies with safety requirements which, in the opinion of that Administration, are adequate for the voyage which is to be undertaken by the ship.

Article 7
Force majeure

(1) A ship which is not subject to the provisions of the present Convention at the time of its departure on any voyage shall not become subject to such provisions on account of any deviation from its intended voyage due to stress of weather or any other cause of *force majeure*.

(2) In applying the provisions of the present Convention, the Contracting Government shall give due consideration to any deviation or delay caused to any ship owing to stress of weather or any other cause of *force majeure*.

Article 8
Equivalents

(1) The Administration may allow any fitting, material, appliance or apparatus to be fitted, or any other provision to be made in a ship, other than that required by the present Convention, if it is satisfied by trial thereof or otherwise that such fitting, material, appliance or apparatus, or provision, is at least as effective as that required by the Convention.

(2) The Administration which allows a fitting, material, appliance or apparatus, or provision, other than that required by the present Convention, shall communicate to the Organization for circulation to the Contracting Governments particulars thereof, together with a report on any trials made.

Article 9
Approvals for experimental purposes

(1) Nothing in the present Convention shall prevent an Administration from making specific approvals for experimental purposes in respect of a ship to which the Convention applies.

(2) An Administration which makes any such approval shall communicate to the Organization for circulation to the Contracting Governments particulars thereof.

---

* The name of the Organization was changed to "International Maritime Organization" by virtue of amendments to the Organization's Convention which entered into force on 22 May 1982.

Article 10
Repairs, alterations and modifications

(1)   A ship which undergoes repairs, alterations, modifications and outfitting related thereto shall continue to comply with at least the requirements previously applicable to the ship. An existing ship in such a case shall not, as a rule, comply to a lesser extent with the requirements for a new ship than it did before.

(2)   Repairs, alterations and modifications of a major character and outfitting related thereto should meet the requirements for a new ship in so far as the Administration deems reasonable and practicable.

Article 11
Zones and areas

(1)   A ship to which the present Convention applies shall comply with the requirements applicable to that ship in the zones and areas described in annex II.

(2)   A port standing on the boundary line between two zones or areas shall be regarded as within the zone or area from or into which the ship arrives or departs.

Article 12
Submersion

(1)   Except as provided in paragraphs (2) and (3) of this article, the appropriate load lines on the sides of the ship corresponding to the season of the year and the zone or area in which the ship may be shall not be submerged at any time when the ship puts to sea, during the voyage or on arrival.

(2)   When a ship is in fresh water of unit density the appropriate load line may be submerged by the amount of the fresh water allowance shown on the International Load Line Certificate (1966). Where the density is other than unity, an allowance shall be made proportional to the difference between 1.025 and the actual density.

(3)   When a ship departs from a port situated on a river or inland waters, deeper loading shall be permitted corresponding to the weight of fuel and all other materials required for consumption between the point of departure and the sea.

Article 13
Survey, inspection and marking

The survey, inspection and marking of ships, as regards the enforcement of the provisions of the present Convention and the granting of exemptions therefrom, shall be carried out by officers of the Administration. The Administration may, however, entrust the survey, inspection and marking either to surveyors nominated for the purpose or to organizations recognized by it. In every case the Administration concerned fully guarantees the completeness and efficiency of the survey, inspection and marking.

Article 14
Initial and periodical surveys and inspections

(1)   A ship shall be subjected to the surveys and inspections specified below:

(a)   A survey before the ship is put in service, which shall include a complete inspection of its structure and equipment insofar as the ship is covered by the present Convention. This survey shall be such as to ensure that the arrangements, material, and scantlings fully comply with the requirements of the present Convention.

(b)   A periodical survey at intervals specified by the Administration, but not exceeding five years, which shall be such as to ensure that the structure, equipment, arrangements, materials and scantlings fully comply with the requirements of the present Convention.

(c)   An periodical inspection within 3 months either way of each annual anniversary date of the certificate to ensure that alterations have not been made to the hull or superstructures which would affect the calculations determining the position of the load line and so as to ensure the maintenance in an effective condition of fittings and appliances for:

(i)   protection of openings;

(ii)   guard rails;

(iii)   freeing ports; and

(iv)   means of access to crew's quarters.

(2)   The periodical inspections referred to in paragraph (1)(c) of this article shall be endorsed on the International Load Line Certificate (1966) or on the International Load Line Exemption Certificate issued to a ship exempted under paragraph (2) of article 6 of the present Convention.

Article 15
Maintenance of conditions after survey

After any survey of the ship under article 14 has been completed, no change shall be made in the structure, equipment, arrangements, material or scantlings covered by the survey, without the sanction of the Administration.

Article 16
Issue of certificates

(1)   An International Load Line Certificate (1966) shall be issued to every ship which has been surveyed and marked in accordance with the present Convention.

(2)   An International Load Line Exemption Certificate shall be issued to any ship to which an exemption has been granted under and in accordance with paragraph (2) or (4) of article 6.

(3)   Such certificates shall be issued by the Administration or by any person or organization duly authorized by it. In every case, the Administration assumes full responsibility for the certificate.

(4)   Notwithstanding any other provision of the present Convention, any international load line certificate which is current when the present Convention comes into force in respect of the Government of the State whose flag the ship is flying shall remain valid for two years or until it expires, whichever is earlier. After that time an International Load Line Certificate (1966) shall be required.

Article 17
Issue of certificate by another Government

(1)   A Contracting Government may, at the request of another Contracting Government, cause a ship to be surveyed and, if satisfied that the provisions of the present Convention are complied with, shall issue or authorize the issue of an International Load Line Certificate (1966) to the ship in accordance with the present Convention.

(2)   A copy of the certificate, a copy of the survey report used for computing the freeboard, and a copy of the computations shall be transmitted as early as possible to the requesting Government.

(3)   A certificate so issued must contain a statement to the effect that it has been issued at the request of the Government of the State whose flag the ship is or will be flying and it shall have the same force and receive the same recognition as a certificate issued under article 16.

(4)   No International Load Line Certificate (1966) shall be issued to a ship which is flying the flag of a State the Government of which is not a Contracting Government.

Article 18
Form of certificates

(1)   The certificates shall be drawn up in the official language or languages of the issuing country. If the language used is neither English nor French, the text shall include a translation into one of these languages.

(2)   The form of the certificates shall be that of the models given in annex III. The arrangement of the printed part of each model certificate shall be exactly reproduced in any certificates issued, and in any certified copies thereof.

---
see also the unified interpretation

Article 19
Duration of certificates

(1)   An International Load Line Certificate (1966) shall be issued for a period specified by the Administration, which shall not exceed 5 years from the date of issue.

(2)   If, after the periodical survey referred to in paragraph (1)(b) of article 14, a new certificate cannot be issued to the ship before the expiry of the certificate originally issued, the person or organization carrying out the survey may extend the validity of the original certificate for a period which shall not exceed five months. This extension shall be endorsed on the certificate, and shall be granted only where there have been no alterations in the structure, equipment, arrangements, material or scantlings which affect the ship's freeboard.

(3) An International Load Line Certificate (1966) shall be cancelled by the Administration if any of the following circumstances exist:

(a) material alterations have taken place in the hull or superstructures of the ship such as would necessitate the assignment of an increased freeboard;

(b) the fittings and appliances mentioned in sub-paragraph (c) of paragraph (1) of article 14 are not maintained in an effective condition;

(c) the certificate is not endorsed to show that the ship has been inspected as provided in sub-paragraph (c) of paragraph (1) of article 14;

(d) the structural strength of the ship is lowered to such an extent that the ship is unsafe.

(4) **(a)** The duration of an International Load Line Exemption Certificate issued by an Administration to a ship exempted under paragraph (2) of article 6 shall not exceed five years from the date of issue. Such certificate shall be subject to a renewal, endorsement and cancellation procedure similar to that provided for an International Load Line Certificate (1966) under this article.

(b) The duration of an International Load Line Exemption Certificate issued to a ship exempted under paragraph (4) of article 6 shall be limited to the single voyage for which it is issued.

(5) A certificate issued to a ship by an Administration shall cease to be valid upon the transfer of such a ship to the flag of another State.

Article 20
Acceptance of certificates

The certificates issued under the authority of a Contracting Government in accordance with the present Convention shall be accepted by the other Contracting Governments and regarded for all purposes covered by the present Convention as having the same force as certificates issued by them.

Article 21
Control

(1) Ships holding a certificate issued under article 16 or article 17 are subject, when in the ports of other Contracting Governments, to control by officers duly authorized by such Governments. Contracting Governments shall ensure that such control is exercised as far as is reasonable and practicable with a view to verifying that there is on board a valid certificate under the present Convention. If there is a valid International Load Line Certificate (1966) on board the ship, such control shall be limited to the purpose of determining that:

(a) the ship is not loaded beyond the limits allowed by the certificate;

(b) the position of the load line of the ship corresponds with the certificate; and

(c) the ship has not been so materially altered in respect of the matters set out in sub-paragraphs (a) and (b) of paragraph (3) of article 19 that the ship is manifestly unfit to proceed to sea without danger to human life.

If there is a valid International Load Line Exemption Certificate on board, such control shall be limited to the purpose of determining that any conditions stipulated in that certificate are complied with.

(2) If such control is exercised under sub-paragraph (c) of paragraph (1) of this article, it shall only be exercised in so far as may be necessary to ensure that the ship shall not sail until it can proceed to sea without danger to the passengers or the crew.

(3) In the event of the control provided for in this article giving rise to intervention of any kind, the officer carrying out the control shall immediately inform in writing the Consul or the diplomatic representative of the State whose flag the ship is flying of this decision and of all the circumstances in which intervention was deemed to be necessary.

Article 22
Privileges

The privileges of the present Convention may not be claimed in favour of any ship unless it holds a valid certificate under the Convention.

Article 23
Casualties

(1) Each Administration undertakes to conduct an investigation of any casualty occurring to ships for which it is responsible and which are subject to the provisions of the present Convention when it judges that such an investigation may assist in determining what changes in the Convention might be desirable.

(2) Each Contracting Government undertakes to supply the Organization with the pertinent information concerning the findings of such investigations. No reports or recommendations of the Organization based upon such information shall disclose the identity or nationality of the ships concerned or in any manner fix or imply responsibility upon any ship or person.

Article 24
Prior treaties and conventions

(1) All other treaties, conventions and arrangements relating to load line matters at present in force between Governments Parties to the present Convention shall continue to have full and complete effect during the terms thereof as regards:

> **(a)** ships to which the present Convention does not apply; and

> **(b)** ships to which the present Convention applies, in respect of matters for which it has not expressly provided.

(2) To the extent, however, that such treaties, conventions or arrangements conflict with the provisions of the present Convention, the provisions of the present Convention shall prevail.

Article 25
Special rules drawn up by agreement

When in accordance with the present Convention special rules are drawn up by agreement among all or some of the Contracting Governments, such rules shall be communicated to the Organization for circulation to all Contracting Governments.

Article 26
Communication of information

(1) The Contracting Governments undertake to communicate to and deposit with the Organization:

> **(a)** a sufficient number of specimens of their certificates issued under the provisions of the present Convention for circulation to the Contracting Governments;

> **(b)** the text of the laws, decrees, orders, regulations and other instruments which shall have been promulgated on the various matters within the scope of the present Convention; and

> **(c)** a list of non-governmental agencies which are authorized to act in their behalf in the administration of load line matters for circulation to the Contracting Governments.

(2) Each Contracting Government agrees to make its strength standards available to any other Contracting Government, upon request.

Article 27
Signature, acceptance and accession

(1) The present Convention shall remain open for signature for three months from 5 April 1966 and shall thereafter remain open for accession. Governments of States Members of the United Nations, or of any of the

Specialized Agencies, or of the International Atomic Energy Agency, or parties to the Statute of the International Court of Justice may become parties to the Convention by:

    (a) signature without reservation as to acceptance;

    (b) signature subject to acceptance followed by acceptance; or

    (c) accession.

(2)   Acceptance or accession shall be effected by the deposit of an instrument of acceptance or accession with the Organization which shall inform all Governments that have signed the Convention or acceded to it of each new acceptance or accession and of the date of its deposit.

Article 28
Coming into force

(1)   The present Convention shall come into force twelve months after the date on which not less than fifteen Governments of the States, including seven each with not less than one million gross tons of shipping, have signed without reservation as to acceptance or deposited instruments of acceptance or accession in accordance with article 27. The Organization shall inform all Governments which have signed or acceded to the present Convention of the date on which it comes into force.

(2)   For Governments which have deposited an instrument of acceptance of or accession to the present Convention during the twelve months mentioned in paragraph (1) of this article, the acceptance or accession shall take effect on the coming into force of the present Convention or three months after the date of deposit of the instrument of acceptance or accession, whichever is the later date.

(3)   For Governments which have deposited an instrument of acceptance of or accession to the present Convention after the date on which it comes into force, the Convention shall come into force three months after the date of the deposit of such instrument.

(4)   After the date on which all the measures required to bring an amendment to the present Convention into force have been completed, or all necessary acceptances are deemed to have been given under sub-paragraph (b) of paragraph (2) of article 29 in case of amendment by unanimous acceptance, any instrument of acceptance or accession deposited shall be deemed to apply to the Convention as amended.

Article 29
Amendments

(1)   The present Convention may be amended upon the proposal of a Contracting Government by any of the procedures specified in this article.

(2)   Amendment by unanimous acceptance:

    (a) Upon the request of a Contracting Government, any amendment proposed by it to the present Convention shall be communicated

13

by the Organization to all Contracting Governments for consideration with a view to unanimous acceptance.

(b) Any such amendment shall enter into force twelve months after the date of its acceptance by all Contracting Governments unless an earlier date is agreed upon. A Contracting Government which does not communicate its acceptance or rejection of the amendment to the Organization within three years of its first communication by the latter shall be deemed to have accepted the amendment.

(c) Any proposed amendment shall be deemed to be rejected if it is not accepted under sub-paragraph (b) of the present paragraph within three years after it has been first communicated to all Contracting Governments by the Organization.

(3)   Amendment after consideration in the Organization:

(a) Upon the request of a Contracting Government, any amendment proposed by it to the present Convention will be considered in the Organization. If adopted by a majority of two-thirds of those present and voting in the Maritime Safety Committee of the Organization, such amendment shall be communicated to all Members of the Organization and all Contracting Governments at least six months prior to its consideration by the Assembly of the Organization.

(b) If adopted by a two-thirds majority of those present and voting in the Assembly, the amendment shall be communicated by the Organization to all Contracting Governments for their acceptance.

(c) Such amendment shall come into force twelve months after the date on which it is accepted by two-thirds of the Contracting Governments. The amendment shall come into force with respect to all Contracting Governments except those which, before it comes into force, make a declaration that they do not accept the amendment.

(d) The Assembly, by a two-thirds majority of those present and voting, including two-thirds of the Governments represented on the Maritime Safety Committee and present and voting in the Assembly, may propose a determination at the time of its adoption that an amendment is of such an important nature that any Contracting Government which makes a declaration under sub-paragraph (c), and which does not accept the amendment within a period of twelve months after it comes into force, shall cease to be a party to the present Convention upon the expiry of that period. This determination shall be subject to the prior acceptance of two-thirds of the Contracting Governments to the present Convention.

(e) Nothing in this paragraph shall prevent the Contracting Government which first proposed action under this paragraph on an amendment to the present Convention from taking at any time such alternative action as it deems desirable in accordance with paragraph (2) or (4) of this article.

(4) Amendment by a conference:

    (a) Upon the request of a Contracting Government, concurred in by at least one-third of the Contracting Governments, a conference of Governments will be convened by the Organization to consider amendments to the present Convention.

    (b) Every amendment adopted by such a conference by a two-thirds majority of those present and voting of the Contracting Governments shall be communicated by the Organization to all Contracting Governments for their acceptance.

    (c) Such amendment shall come into force twelve months after the date on which it is accepted by two-thirds of the Contracting Governments. The amendment shall come into force with respect to all Contracting Governments except those which, before it comes into force, make a declaration that they do not accept the amendment.

    (d) By a two-thirds majority of those present and voting, a conference convened under sub-paragraph (a) may determine at the time of its adoption that an amendment is of such an important nature that any Contracting Government which makes a declaration under sub-paragraph (c), and which does not accept the amendment within a period of twelve months after it comes into force, shall cease to be a party to the present Convention upon the expiry of that period.

(5) Any amendments to the present Convention made under this article which relate to the structure of a ship shall apply only to ships the keels of which are laid, or which are at a similar stage of construction, on or after the date on which the amendment comes into force.

(6) The Organization shall inform all Contracting Governments of any amendments which come into force under this article, together with the date on which each such amendment will come into force.

(7) Any acceptance or declaration under this article shall be made by a notification in writing to the Organization which shall notify all Contracting Governments of the receipt of the acceptance or declaration.

Article 30
Denunciation

(1) The present Convention may be denounced by any Contracting Government at any time after the expiry of five years from the date on which the Convention comes into force for that Government.

(2) Denunciation shall be effected by a notification in writing addressed to the Organization which shall inform all the other Contracting Governments of any such notification received and of the date of its receipt.

(3) A denunciation shall take effect one year, or such longer period as may be specified in the notification, after its receipt by the Organization.

Article 31
Suspension

(1) In case of hostilities or other extraordinary circumstances which affect the vital interests of a State the Government of which is a Contracting Government, that Government may suspend the operation of the whole or any part of the present Convention. The suspending Government shall immediately give notice of any such suspension to the Organization.

(2) Such suspension shall not deprive other Contracting Governments of any right of control under the present Convention over the ships of the suspending Government when such ships are within their ports.

(3) The suspending Government may at any time terminate such suspension and shall immediately give notice of such termination to the Organization.

(4) The Organization shall notify all Contracting Governments of any suspension or termination of suspension under this article.

Article 32
Territories

(1) **(a)** The United Nations, in cases where they are the administering authority for a territory, or any Contracting Government responsible for the international relations of a territory, shall as soon as possible consult with such territory in an endeavour to extend the present Convention to that territory and may at any time by notification in writing to the Organization declare that the present Convention shall extend to such territory.

(b) The present Convention shall, from the date of the receipt of the notification or from such other date as may be specified in the notification, extend to the territory named therein.

(2) **(a)** The United Nations, or any Contracting Government which has made a declaration under sub-paragraph (a) of paragraph (1) of this article, at any time after the expiry of a period of five years from the date on which the Convention has been so extended to any territory, may by notification in writing to the Organization declare that the present Convention shall cease to extend to any such territory named in the notification.

(b) The present Convention shall cease to extend to any territory mentioned in such notification one year, or such longer period as may be specified therein, after the date of receipt of the notification by the Organization.

(3) The Organization shall inform all the Contracting Governments of the extension of the present Convention to any territories under paragraph (1) of this article, and of the termination of any such extension under the provisions of paragraph (2), stating in each case the date from which the present Convention has been or will cease to be so extended.

Article 33
Registration

(1)   The present Convention shall be deposited with the Organization and the Secretary-General of the Organization shall transmit certified true copies thereof to all Signatory Governments and to all Governments which accede to the present Convention.

(2)   As soon as the present Convention comes into force it shall be registered by the Organization in accordance with Article 102 of the Charter of the United Nations.

Article 34
Languages

The present Convention is established in a single copy in the English and French languages, both texts being equally authentic. Official translations in the Russian and Spanish languages shall be prepared and deposited with the signed original.

IN WITNESS WHEREOF the undersigned being duly authorized by their respective Governments for that purpose have signed the present Convention.[*]

DONE at London this fifth day of April 1966.

_____

[*] Signatures omitted.

Annex I
Regulations for determining load lines

Chapter I
General

The regulations assume that the nature and stowage of the cargo, ballast, etc., are such as to secure sufficient stability of the ship and the avoidance of excessive structural stress.

The regulations also assume that where there are international requirements relating to stability or subdivision, these requirements have been complied with.

Regulation 1
Strength of hull

The Administration shall satisfy itself that the general structural strength of the hull is sufficient for the draught corresponding to the freeboard assigned. Ships built and maintained in conformity with the requirements of a classification society recognized by the Administration may be considered to possess adequate strength.

Regulation 2
Application

(1) Ships with mechanical means of propulsion or lighters, barges or other ships without independent means of propulsion shall be assigned freeboards in accordance with the provisions of regulations 1–40 inclusive of this annex.

(2) Ships carrying timber deck cargoes may be assigned, in addition to the freeboards prescribed in paragraph (1) of this regulation, timber freeboards in accordance with the provisions of regulations 41–45 inclusive of this annex.

(3) Ships designed to carry sail, whether as the sole means of propulsion or as a supplementary means, and tugs, shall be assigned freeboards in accordance with the provisions of regulations 1–40 inclusive of this annex. Such additional freeboard shall be required as determined by the Administration.

(4) Ships of wood or of composite construction, or of other materials the use of which the Administration has approved, or ships whose constructional features are such as to render the application of the provisions of this annex unreasonable or impracticable, shall be assigned freeboards as determined by the Administration.

(5) Regulations 10–26 inclusive of this annex shall apply to every ship to which a minimum freeboard is assigned. Relaxations from these requirements may be granted to a ship to which a greater than minimum freeboard is assigned on condition that the Administration is satisfied with the safety conditions provided.

---
see also the unified interpretation

Regulation 3
Definitions of terms used in the annexes

(1) *Length.* The length (L) shall be taken as 96% of the total length on a waterline at 85% of the least moulded depth measured from the top of the keel, or as the length from the fore side of the stem to the axis of the rudder stock on that waterline, if that be greater. In ships designed with a rake of keel the waterline on which this length is measured shall be parallel to the designed waterline.

(2) *Perpendiculars.* The forward and after perpendiculars shall be taken at the forward and after ends of the length (L). The forward perpendicular shall coincide with the fore side of the stem on the waterline on which the length is measured.

(3) *Amidships.* Amidships is at the middle of the length (L).

(4) *Breadth.* Unless expressly provided otherwise, the breadth (B) is the maximum breadth of the ship, measured amidships to the moulded line of the frame in a ship with a metal shell and to the outer surface of the hull in a ship with a shell of any other material.

(5) *Moulded depth*

(a) The moulded depth is the vertical distance measured from the top of the keel to the top of the freeboard deck beam at side. In wood and composite ships the distance is measured from the lower edge of the keel rabbet. Where the form at the lower part of the midship section is of a hollow character, or where thick garboards are fitted, the distance is measured from the point where the line of the flat of the bottom continued inwards cuts the side of the keel.

(b) In ships having rounded gunwales, the moulded depth shall be measured to the point of intersection of the moulded lines of the deck and side shell plating, the lines extending as though the gunwale were of angular design.

(c) Where the freeboard deck is stepped and the raised part of the deck extends over the point at which the moulded depth is to be determined, the moulded depth shall be measured to a line of reference extending from the lower part of the deck along a line parallel with the raised part.

---
see also the unified interpretation

---

(6) *Depth for freeboard (D)*

(a) The depth for freeboard (D) is the moulded depth amidships, plus the thickness of the freeboard deck stringer plate, where fitted, plus $\dfrac{T(L - S)}{L}$ if the exposed freeboard deck is sheathed, where

T is the mean thickness of the exposed sheathing clear of deck openings, and

S is the total length of superstructures as defined in sub-paragraph (10)(d) of this regulation.

(b) The depth for freeboard (D) in a ship having a rounded gunwale with a radius greater than 4% of the breadth (B) or having topsides of unusual form is the depth for freeboard of a ship having a midship section with vertical topsides and with the same round of beam and area of topside section equal to that provided by the actual midship section.

---
see also the unified interpretation
---

(7) *Block coefficient.* The block coefficient (C_b) is given by:

$$C_b = \frac{\nabla}{L \cdot B \cdot d_1}; \text{ where}$$

∇ is the volume of the moulded displacement of the ship, excluding bossing, in a ship with a metal shell, and is the volume of displacement to the outer surface of the hull in a ship with a shell of any other material, both taken at a moulded draught of d_1; and where

d_1 is 85% of the least moulded depth.

(8)   *Freeboard.* The freeboard assigned is the distance measured vertically downwards amidships from the upper edge of the deck line to the upper edge of the related load line.

(9)   *Freeboard deck.* The freeboard deck is normally the uppermost complete deck exposed to weather and sea, which has permanent means of closing all openings in the weather part thereof, and below which all openings in the sides of the ship are fitted with permanent means of watertight closing. In a ship having a discontinuous freeboard deck, the lowest line of the exposed deck and the continuation of that line parallel to the upper part of the deck is taken as the freeboard deck. At the option of the owner and subject to the approval of the Administration, a lower deck may be designated as the freeboard deck provided it is a complete and permanent deck continuous in a fore and aft direction at least between the machinery space and peak bulkheads and continuous athwartships. When this lower deck is stepped the lowest line of the deck and the continuation of that line parallel to the upper part of the deck is taken as the freeboard deck. When a lower deck is designated as the freeboard deck, that part of the hull which extends above the freeboard deck is treated as a superstructure so far as concerns the application of the conditions of assignment and the calculation of freeboard. It is from this deck that the freeboard is calculated.

---
see also the unified interpretations
---

(10) *Superstructure*

(a) A superstructure is a decked structure on the freeboard deck, extending from side to side of the ship or with the side plating not being inboard of the shell plating more than 4% of the breadth (*B*). A raised quarter-deck is regarded as a superstructure.

(b) An enclosed superstructure is a superstructure with:

(i) enclosing bulkheads of efficient construction;

(ii) access openings, if any, in these bulkheads fitted with doors complying with the requirements of regulation 12;

(iii) all other openings in sides or ends of the superstructure fitted with efficient weathertight means of closing.

A bridge or poop shall not be regarded as enclosed unless access is provided for the crew to reach machinery and other working spaces inside these superstructures by alternative means which are available at all times when bulkhead openings are closed.

---
see also the unified interpretation

(c) The height of a superstructure is the least vertical height measured at side from the top of the superstructure deck beams to the top of the freeboard deck beams.

(d) The length of a superstructure (*S*) is the mean length of the part of the superstructure which lies within the length (*L*).

(11) *Flush deck ship*. A flush deck ship is one which has no superstructure on the freeboard deck.

(12) *Weathertight*. "Weathertight" means that in any sea conditions water will not penetrate into the ship.

Regulation 4
Deck line

The deck line is a horizontal line 300 mm (12 inches) in length and 25 mm (1 inch) in breadth. It shall be marked amidships on each side of the ship, and its upper edge shall normally pass through the point where the continuation outwards of the upper surface of the freeboard deck intersects the outer surface of the shell (as illustrated in figure 1), provided that the deck line may be placed with reference to another fixed point on the ship on condition that the freeboard is correspondingly corrected. The location of the reference point and the identification of the freeboard deck shall in all cases be indicated on the International Load Line Certificate (1966).

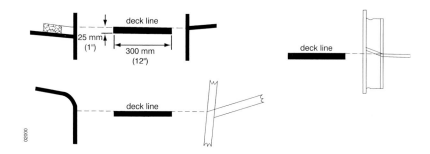

Figure 1 – *Deck line*

Regulation 5
Load Line Mark

The Load Line Mark shall consist of a ring 300 mm (12 inches) in outside diameter and 25 mm (1 inch) wide which is intersected by a horizontal line 450 mm (18 inches) in length and 25 mm (1 inch) in breadth, the upper edge of which passes through the centre of the ring. The centre of the ring shall be placed amidships and at a distance equal to the assigned summer freeboard measured vertically below the upper edge of the deck line (as illustrated in figure 2).

Regulation 6
Lines to be used with the Load Line Mark

(1)   The lines which indicate the load line assigned in accordance with these regulations shall be horizontal lines 230 mm (9 inches) in length and 25 mm (1 inch) in breadth which extend forward of, unless expressly provided otherwise, and at right angles to, a vertical line 25 mm (1 inch) in breadth marked at a distance 540 mm (21 inches) forward of the centre of the ring (as illustrated in figure 2).

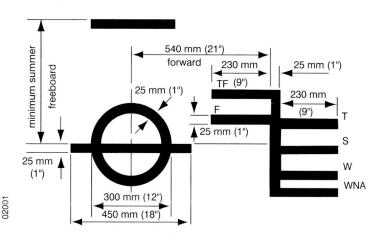

Figure 2 – *Load Line Mark and lines to be used with this mark*

23

(2)   The following load lines shall be used:

(a)   The Summer Load Line indicated by the upper edge of the line which passes through the centre of the ring and also by a line marked **S**.

(b)   The Winter Load Line indicated by the upper edge of a line marked **W**.

(c)   The Winter North Atlantic Load Line indicated by the upper edge of a line marked **WNA**.

(d)   The Tropical Load Line indicated by the upper edge of a line marked **T**.

(e)   The Fresh Water Load Line in summer indicated by the upper edge of a line marked **F**. The Fresh Water Load Line in summer is marked abaft the vertical line. The difference between the Fresh Water Load Line in summer and the Summer Load Line is the allowance to be made for loading in fresh water at the other load lines.

(f)   The Tropical Fresh Water Load Line indicated by the upper edge of a line marked **TF**, and marked abaft the vertical line.

(3)   If timber freeboards are assigned in accordance with these regulations, the timber load lines shall be marked in addition to ordinary load lines. These lines shall be horizontal lines 230 mm (9 inches) in length and 25 mm (1 inch) in breadth which extend abaft unless expressly provided otherwise, and are at right angles to, a vertical line 25 mm (1 inch) in breadth marked at a distance 540 mm (21 inches) abaft the centre of the ring (as illustrated in figure 3).

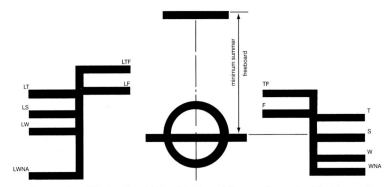

Figure 3 – *Timber Load Line Mark and lines to be used with this mark*

(4)   The following timber load lines shall be used:

(a)   The Summer Timber Load Line indicated by the upper edge of a line marked **LS**.

(b)   The Winter Timber Load Line indicated by the upper edge of a line marked **LW**.

(c)   The Winter North Atlantic Timber Load Line indicated by the upper edge of a line marked **LWNA**.

(d) The Tropical Timber Load Line indicated by the upper edge of a line marked **LT**.

(e) The Fresh Water Timber Load Line in summer indicated by the upper edge of a line marked **LF** and marked forward of the vertical line. The difference between the Fresh Water Timber Load Line in summer and the Summer Timber Load Line is the allowance to be made for loading in fresh water at the other timber load lines.

(f) The Tropical Fresh Water Timber Load Line indicated by the upper edge of a line marked **LTF** and marked forward of the vertical line.

(5) Where the characteristics of a ship or the nature of the ship's service or navigational limits make any of the seasonal lines inapplicable, these lines may be omitted.

(6) Where a ship is assigned a greater than minimum freeboard so that the load line is marked at a position corresponding to, or lower than, the lowest seasonal load line assigned at minimum freeboard in accordance with the present Convention, only the Fresh Water Load Line need be marked.

(7) On sailing ships only the Fresh Water Load Line and the Winter North Atlantic Load Line need be marked (as illustrated in figure 4).

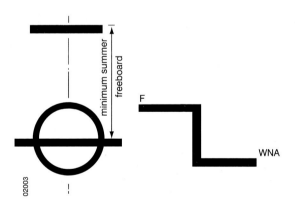

Figure 4 – *Load Line Mark on sailing ships and lines to be used with this mark*

(8) Where a Winter North Atlantic Load Line is identical with the Winter Load Line corresponding to the same vertical line, this load line shall be marked **W**.

(9) Additional load lines required by other international conventions in force may be marked at right angles to and abaft the vertical line specified in paragraph (1) of this regulation.

Regulation 7
Mark of assigning Authority

The mark of the Authority by whom the load lines are assigned may be indicated alongside the load line ring above the horizontal line which passes through the centre of the ring, or above and below it. This mark shall consist of not more than four initials to identify the Authority's name, each measuring approximately 115 mm ($4\frac{1}{2}$ inches) in height and 75 mm (3 inches) in width.

Regulation 8
Details of marking

The ring, lines and letters shall be painted in white or yellow on a dark ground or in black on a light ground. They shall also be permanently marked on the sides of the ships to the satisfaction of the Administration. The marks shall be plainly visible and, if necessary, special arrangements shall be made for this purpose.

see also the unified interpretation

Regulation 9
Verification of marks

The International Load Line Certificate (1966) shall not be delivered to the ship until the officer or surveyor acting under the provisions of article 13 of the present Convention has certified that the marks are correctly and permanently indicated on the ship's sides.

Chapter II
Conditions of assignment of freeboard

Regulation 10
Information to be supplied to the master

(1)   The master of every new ship shall be supplied with sufficient information, in an approved form, to enable him to arrange for the loading and ballasting of his ship in such a way as to avoid the creation of any unacceptable stresses in the ship's structure, provided that this requirement need not apply to any particular length, design or class of ship where the Administration considers it to be unnecessary.

(2)   The master of every new ship which is not already provided with stability information under an international convention for the safety of life at sea in force shall be supplied with sufficient information in an approved form to give him guidance as to the stability of the ship under varying conditions of service, and a copy shall be furnished to the Administration.

Regulation 11
Superstructure end bulkheads

Bulkheads at exposed ends of enclosed superstructures shall be of efficient construction and shall be to the satisfaction of the Administration

Regulation 12
Doors

---
see also the unified interpretation
---

(1)   All access openings in bulkheads at ends of enclosed superstructures shall be fitted with doors of steel or other equivalent material, permanently and strongly attached to the bulkhead, and framed, stiffened and fitted so that the whole structure is of equivalent strength to the unpierced bulkhead and weathertight when closed. The means for securing these doors weathertight shall consist of gaskets and clamping devices or other equivalent means and shall be permanently attached to the bulkhead or to the doors themselves, and the doors shall be so arranged that they can be operated from both sides of the bulkhead.

(2)   Except as otherwise provided in these regulations, the height of the sills of access openings in bulkheads at ends of enclosed superstructures shall be at least 380 mm (15 inches) above the deck.

Regulation 13
Position of hatchways, doorways and ventilators

For the purpose of the regulations, two positions of hatchways, doorways and ventilators are defined as follows:

Position 1 – Upon exposed freeboard and raised quarter-decks, and upon exposed superstructure decks situated forward of a point located a quarter of the ship's length from the forward perpendicular.

Position 2 – Upon exposed superstructure decks situated abaft a quarter of the ship's length from the forward perpendicular.

Regulation 14
Cargo and other hatchways

(1)   The construction and the means for securing the weathertightness of cargo and other hatchways in positions 1 and 2 shall be at least equivalent to the requirements of regulations 15 and 16 of this annex.

(2)   Coamings and hatchway covers to exposed hatchways on decks above the superstructure deck shall comply with the requirements of the Administration.

Regulation 15
Hatchways closed by portable covers and secured weathertight by tarpaulins and battening devices

Hatchway coamings

(1)   The coamings of hatchways closed by portable covers secured weathertight by tarpaulins and battening devices shall be of substantial construction, and their height above the deck shall be at least as follows:

600 mm (23$\frac{1}{2}$ inches) if in position 1

450 mm (17$\frac{1}{2}$ inches) if in position 2.

Hatchway covers

(2)   The width of each bearing surface for hatchway covers shall be at least 65 mm (2$\frac{1}{2}$ inches).

(3)   Where covers are made of wood, the finished thickness shall be at least 60 mm (2$\frac{3}{8}$ inches) in association with a span of not more than 1.5 m (4.9 feet).

(4)   Where covers are made of mild steel the strength shall be calculated with assumed loads not less than 1.75 metric tons per square metre (358 pounds per square foot) on hatchways in position 1, and not less than 1.30 metric tons per square metre (266 pounds per square foot) on hatchways in position 2, and the product of the maximum stress thus calculated and the factor 4.25 shall not exceed the minimum ultimate strength of the material. They shall be so designed as to limit the deflection to not more than 0.0028 times the span under these loads.

see also the unified interpretation

(5)   The assumed loads on hatchways in position 1 may be reduced to 1 metric ton per square metre (205 pounds per square foot) for ships of 24 m (79 feet) in length and shall be not less than 1.75 metric tons per square metre (358 pounds per square foot) for ships of 100 m (328 feet) in length. The corresponding loads on hatchways in position 2 may be reduced to 0.75 metric tons per square metre (154 pounds per square foot) and 1.30 metric tons per square metre (266 pounds per square foot) respectively. In all cases values at intermediate lengths shall be obtained by interpolation.

<hr>

see also the unified interpretation

<hr>

Portable beams

(6)   Where portable beams for supporting hatchway covers are made of mild steel the strength shall be calculated with assumed loads not less than 1.75 metric tons per square metre (358 pounds per square foot) on hatchways in position 1 and not less than 1.30 metric tons per square metre (266 pounds per square foot) on hatchways in position 2 and the product of the maximum stress thus calculated and the factor 5 shall not exceed the minimum ultimate strength of the material. They shall be so designed as to limit the deflection to not more than 0.0022 times the span under these loads. For ships of not more than 100 metres (328 feet) in length the requirements of paragraph (5) of this regulation are applicable.

<hr>

see also the unified interpretation

<hr>

Pontoon covers

(7)   Where pontoon covers used in place of portable beams and covers are made of mild steel the strength shall be calculated with the assumed loads given in paragraph (4) of this regulation, and the product of the maximum stress thus calculated and the factor 5 shall not exceed the minimum ultimate strength of the material. They shall be so designed as to limit the deflection to not more than 0.0022 times the span. Mild steel plating forming the tops of covers shall be not less in thickness than 1% of the spacing of stiffeners or 6 mm (0.24 inches) if that be greater. For ships of not more than 100 m (328 feet) in length the requirements of paragraph (5) of this regulation are applicable.

<hr>

see also the unified interpretation

<hr>

(8)   The strength and stiffness of covers made of materials other than mild steel shall be equivalent to those of mild steel to the satisfaction of the Administration.

Carriers or sockets

(9)   Carriers or sockets for portable beams shall be of substantial construction, and shall provide means for the efficient fitting and securing of the beams. Where rolling types of beams are used, the arrangements shall ensure that the beams remain properly in position when the hatchway is closed.

Cleats

(10)   Cleats shall be set to fit the taper of the wedges. They shall be at least 65 mm ($2\frac{1}{2}$ inches) wide and spaced not more than 600 mm ($23\frac{1}{2}$ inches) centre to centre; the cleats along each side or end shall be not more than 150 mm (6 inches) from the hatch corners.

Battens and wedges

(11)   Battens and wedges shall be efficient and in good condition. Wedges shall be of tough wood or other equivalent material. They shall have a taper of not more than 1 in 6 and shall be not less than 13 mm (½ inch) thick at the toes.

Tarpaulins

(12)   At least two layers of tarpaulin in good condition shall be provided for each hatchway in position 1 or 2. The tarpaulins shall be waterproof and of ample strength. They shall be of a material of at least an approved standard weight and quality.

Security of hatchway covers

(13)   For all hatchways in position 1 or 2 steel bars or other equivalent means shall be provided in order efficiently and independently to secure each section of hatchway covers after the tarpaulins are battened down. Hatchway covers of more than 1.5 m (4.9 feet) in length shall be secured by at least two such securing appliances.

---
see also the unified interpretation

Regulation 16
Hatchways closed by weathertight covers of steel or other equivalent material fitted with gaskets and clamping devices

---
see also the unified interpretations

Hatchway coamings

(1)   At positions 1 and 2 the height above the deck of hatchway coamings fitted with weathertight hatch covers of steel or other equivalent material fitted with gaskets and clamping devices shall be as specified in regulation 15(1). The height of these coamings may be reduced, or the coamings omitted entirely, on condition that the Administration is satisfied that the safety of the ship is not thereby impaired in any sea conditions. Where coamings are provided they shall be of substantial construction.

Weathertight covers

(2)   Where weathertight covers are of mild steel the strength shall be calculated with assumed loads not less than 1.75 metric tons per square metre (358 pounds per square foot) on hatchways in position 1, and not less than 1.30 metric tons per square metre (266 pounds per square foot) on hatchways in position 2, and the product of the maximum stress thus calculated and the factor of 4.25 shall not exceed the minimum ultimate strength of the material. They shall be so designed as to limit the deflection to not more than 0.0028 times the span under these loads. Mild steel plating forming the tops of covers shall be not less in thickness than 1% of the spacing of stiffeners or 6 mm (0.24 inches) if that be greater. The provisions of regulation 15(5) are applicable for ships of not more than 100 m (328 feet) in length.

(3)   The strength and stiffness of covers made of materials other than mild steel shall be equivalent to those of mild steel to the satisfaction of the Administration.

Means for securing weathertightness

(4)   The means for securing and maintaining weathertightness shall be to the satisfaction of the Administration. The arrangements shall ensure that the tightness can be maintained in any sea conditions, and for this purpose tests for tightness shall be required at the initial survey, and may be required at periodical surveys and at annual inspections or at more frequent intervals.

Regulation 17
Machinery space openings

(1)   Machinery space openings in position 1 or 2 shall be properly framed and efficiently enclosed by steel casings of ample strength, and where the casings are not protected by other structures their strength shall be specially considered. Access openings in such casings shall be fitted with doors complying with the requirements of regulation 12(1), the sills of which shall be at least 600 mm (23½ inches) above the deck if in position 1, and at least 380 mm (15 inches) above the deck if in position 2. Other openings in such casings shall be fitted with equivalent covers, permanently attached in their proper positions.

---
see also the unified interpretation
---

(2)   Coamings of any fiddley, funnel or machinery space ventilator in an exposed position on the freeboard or superstructure deck shall be as high above the deck as is reasonable and practicable. Fiddley openings shall be fitted with strong covers of steel or other equivalent material permanently attached in their proper positions and capable of being secured weathertight.

---
see also the unified interpretation

Regulation 18
Miscellaneous openings in freeboard and superstructure decks

(1)   Manholes and flush scuttles in position 1 or 2 or within superstructures other than enclosed superstructures shall be closed by substantial covers capable of being made watertight. Unless secured by closely spaced bolts, the covers shall be permanently attached.

(2)   Openings in freeboard decks other than hatchways, machinery space openings, manholes and flush scuttles shall be protected by an enclosed superstructure, or by a deckhouse or companionway of equivalent strength and weathertightness. Any such opening in an exposed superstructure deck, or in the top of a deckhouse on the freeboard deck which gives access to a space below the freeboard deck or a space within an enclosed superstructure shall be protected by an efficient deckhouse or companionway. Doorways in such deckhouses or companionways shall be fitted with doors complying with the requirements of regulation 12(1).

---
see also the unified interpretations
---

(3)   In position 1 the height above the deck of sills to the doorways in companionways shall be at least 600 mm (23½ inches). In position 2 it shall be at least 380 mm (15 inches).

see also the unified interpretation

Regulation 19
Ventilators

see also the unified interpretation

(1)   Ventilators in position 1 or 2 to spaces below freeboard decks or decks of enclosed superstructures shall have coamings of steel or other equivalent material, substantially constructed and efficiently connected to the deck. Where the coaming of any ventilator exceeds 900 mm (35½ inches) in height it shall be specially supported.

(2)   Ventilators passing through superstructures other than enclosed superstructures shall have substantially constructed coamings of steel or other equivalent material at the freeboard deck.

(3)   Ventilators in position 1 the coamings of which extend to more than 4.5 m (14.8 feet) above the deck, and in position 2 the coamings of which extend to more than 2.3 m (7.5 feet) above the deck, need not be fitted with closing arrangements unless specifically required by the Administration.

see also the unified interpretation

(4)   Except as provided in paragraph (3) of this regulation, ventilator openings shall be provided with weathertight closing appliances. In ships of not more than 100 m (328 feet) in length the closing appliances shall be permanently attached; where not so provided in other ships, they shall be conveniently stowed near the ventilators to which they are to be fitted. Ventilators in position 1 shall have coamings of a height of at least 900 mm (35½ inches) above the deck; in position 2 the coamings shall be of a height at least 760 mm (30 inches) above the deck.

see also the unified interpretation

(5)   In exposed positions, the height of coamings may be required to be increased to the satisfaction of the Administration.

Regulation 20
Air pipes

Where air pipes to ballast and other tanks extend above the freeboard or superstructure decks, the exposed parts of the pipes shall be of substantial construction; the height from the deck to the point where water may have access below shall be at least 760 mm (30 inches) on the freeboard deck and 450 mm (17½ inches) on the superstructure deck. Where these heights may interfere with the working of the ship, a lower height may be approved, provided the Administration is satisfied that the closing arrangements and other circumstances justify a lower height. Satisfactory means, permanently attached, shall be provided for closing the openings of the air pipes.

see also the unified interpretations

Regulation 21
Cargo ports and other similar openings

see also the unified interpretation

(1)   Cargo ports and other similar openings in the sides of ships below the freeboard deck shall be fitted with doors so designed as to ensure watertightness and structural integrity commensurate with the surrounding shell plating. The number of such openings shall be the minimum compatible with the design and proper working of the ship.

see also the unified interpretation

(2)   Unless permitted by the Administration, the lower edge of such openings shall not be below a line drawn parallel to the freeboard deck at side, which has at its lowest point the upper edge of the uppermost load line.

see also the unified interpretation

Regulation 22
Scuppers, inlets and discharges

see also the unified interpretation

(1)   Discharges led through the shell either from spaces below the freeboard deck or from within superstructures and deckhouses on the freeboard deck fitted with doors complying with the requirements of regulation 12 shall, be fitted with efficient and accessible means for preventing water from passing inboard. Normally each separate discharge shall have one automatic non-return valve with a positive means of closing it from a position above the freeboard deck. Where, however, the vertical distance from the summer load waterline to the inboard end of the discharge pipe exceeds $0.01L$, the discharge may have two automatic non-return valves without positive means of closing, provided that the inboard valve is always accessible for examination under service conditions; where that vertical distance exceeds $0.02L$, a single automatic non-return valve without positive means of closing may be accepted subject to the approval of the Administration. The means for operating the positive-action valve shall be readily accessible and provided with an indicator showing whether the valve is open or closed.

see also the unified interpretations

(2)   In manned machinery spaces, main and auxiliary sea inlets and discharges in connection with the operation of machinery may be controlled locally. The controls shall be readily accessible and shall be provided with indicators showing whether the valves are open or closed.

(3)   Scuppers and discharge pipes originating at any level and penetrating the shell either more than 450 mm (17½ inches) below the freeboard deck or less than 600 mm (23½ inches) above the summer load waterline shall be provided with a non-return valve at the shell. This valve, unless required by paragraph (1), may be omitted if the piping is of substantial thickness.

(4)   Scuppers leading from superstructures or deckhouses not fitted with doors complying with the requirements of regulation 12 shall be led overboard.

(5)   All valves and shell fittings required by this regulation shall be of steel, bronze or other approved ductile material. Valves of ordinary cast iron or similar material are not acceptable. All pipes to which this regulation refers shall be of steel or other equivalent material to the satisfaction of the Administration.

Regulation 23
Sidescuttles

---
see also the unified interpretations
---

(1)   Sidescuttles to spaces below the freeboard deck or to spaces within enclosed superstructures shall be fitted with efficient hinged inside deadlights arranged so that they can be effectively closed and secured watertight.

(2)   No sidescuttle shall be fitted in a position so that its sill is below a line drawn parallel to the freeboard deck at side and having its lowest point 2.5% of the breadth (B) above the load waterline or 500 mm (19½ inches), whichever is the greater distance.

(3)   The sidescuttles, together with their glasses, if fitted, and deadlights, shall be of substantial and approved construction.

Regulation 24
Freeing ports

(1)   Where bulwarks on the weather portions of freeboard or super-structure decks form wells, ample provision shall be made for rapidly freeing the decks of water and for draining them. Except as provided in paragraphs (2) and (3) of this regulation, the minimum freeing port area (A) on each side of the ship for each well on the freeboard deck shall be that given by the following formulae in cases where the sheer in way of the well is standard or greater than standard. The minimum area for each well on superstructure decks shall be one-half of the area given by the formulae.

Where the length of bulwark (l) in the well is 20 m or less

$$A = 0.7 + 0.035l \text{ m}^2.$$

Where l exceeds 20 m

$$A = 0.07l \text{ m}^2.$$

l need in no case be taken as greater than $0.7L$.

If the bulwark is more than 1.2 m in average height, the required area shall be increased by 0.004 m² per metre of length of well for each 0.1 m difference in height. If the bulwark is less than 0.9 m in average height, the required area may be decreased by 0.004 m^2 per metre of length of well for each 0.1 m difference in height.

Or

Where the length of bulwark (*l*) in the well is 66 feet or less

$A = 7.6 + 0.115l$ (square feet).

Where *l* exceeds 66 feet

$A = 0.23l$ (square feet)

l need in no case be taken as greater than 0.7L.

If the bulwark is more than 3.9 feet in average height, the required area shall be increased by 0.04 square feet per foot of length of well for each foot difference in height. If the bulwark is less than 3 feet in average height, the required area may be decreased by 0.04 square feet per foot of length for each foot difference in height.

---
see also the unified interpretations
---

(2)   In ships with no sheer, the calculated area shall be increased by 50%. Where the sheer is less than the standard, the percentage shall be obtained by interpolation.

(3)   Where a ship fitted with a trunk does not comply with the requirements of regulation 36(1)(e) or where continuous or substantially continuous hatchway side coamings are fitted between detached super-structures, the minimum area of the freeing port openings shall be calculated from the following table:

Breadth of hatchway or trunk in relation to the breadth of ship	Area of freeing ports in relation to the total area of the bulwarks
40% or less	20%
75% or more	10%

The area of freeing ports at intermediate breadths shall be obtained by linear interpolation.

---
see also the unified interpretation
---

(4)   In ships having superstructures which are open at either or both ends, adequate provision for freeing the space within such superstructures shall be provided to the satisfaction of the Administration.

---
see also the unified interpretation
---

(5)   The lower edges of the freeing ports shall be as near the deck as practicable. Two-thirds of the freeing port area required shall be provided in the half of the well nearest the lowest point of the sheer curve.

---
see also the unified interpretation
---

(6) All such openings in the bulwarks shall be protected by rails or bars spaced approximately 230 mm (9 inches) apart. If shutters are fitted to freeing ports, ample clearance shall be provided to prevent jamming. Hinges shall have pins or bearings of non-corrodible material. If shutters are fitted with securing appliances, these appliances shall be of approved construction.

Regulation 25
Protection of the crew

(1) The strength of the deckhouses used for the accommodation of the crew shall be to the satisfaction of the Administration.

(2) Efficient guard rails or bulwarks shall be fitted to all exposed parts of the freeboard and superstructure decks. The height of the bulwarks or guard rails shall be at least 1 m ($39\frac{1}{2}$ inches) from the deck, provided that where this height would interfere with the normal operation of the ship, a lesser height may be approved if the Administration is satisfied that adequate protection is provided.

---
see also the unified interpretations
---

(3) The opening below the lowest course of the guard rails shall not exceed 230 mm (9 inches). The other courses shall be not more than 380 mm (15 inches) apart. In the case of ships with rounded gunwales the guard rail supports shall be placed on the flat of the deck.

---
see also the unified interpretation
---

(4) Satisfactory means (in the form of guard rails, lifelines, gangways or underdeck passages, etc.) shall be provided for the protection of the crew in getting to and from their quarters, the machinery space and all other parts used in the necessary work of the ship.

---
see also the unified interpretation
---

(5) Deck cargo carried on any ship shall be so stowed that any opening which is in way of the cargo and which gives access to and from the crew's quarters, the machinery space and all other parts used in the necessary work of the ship, can be properly closed and secured against the admission of water. Effective protection for the crew in the form of guard rails or lifelines shall be provided above the deck cargo if there is no convenient passage on or below the deck of the ship.

Regulation 26
Special conditions of assignment for type 'A' ships

---
see also the unified interpretation

Machinery casings

(1) Machinery casings on type 'A' ships, as defined in regulation 27, shall be protected by an enclosed poop or bridge of at least standard height, or by a deckhouse of equal height and equivalent strength, provided that machinery casings may be exposed if there are no openings giving direct access from the freeboard deck to the machinery space. A door complying with the requirements of regulation 12 may, however, be permitted in the machinery casing, provided that it leads to a space or passageway which is as strongly constructed as the casing and is separated from the stairway to the engine-room by a second weathertight door of steel or other equivalent material.

see also the unified interpretation

Gangway and access

(2)   An efficiently constructed fore and aft permanent gangway sufficient strength shall be fitted on type 'A' ships at the level of the superstructure deck between the poop and the midship bridge or deckhouse where fitted, or equivalent means of access shall be provided to carry out the purpose of the gangway, such as passages below deck. Elsewhere, and on type 'A' ships without a midship bridge, arrangements to the satisfaction of the Administration shall be provided to safeguard the crew in reaching all parts used in the necessary work of the ship.

see also the unified interpretation

(3)   Safe and satisfactory access from the gangway level shall be available between separate crew accommodations and also between crew accommodations and the machinery space.

Hatchways

(4)   Exposed hatchways on the freeboard and forecastle decks or on the tops of expansion trunks on type 'A' ships shall be provided with efficient watertight covers of steel or other equivalent material.

Freeing arrangements

(5)   Type 'A' ships with bulwarks shall have open rails fitted for at least half the length of the exposed parts of the weather deck or other effective freeing arrangements. The upper edge of the sheer strake shall be kept as low as practicable.

see also the unified interpretation

(6)   Where superstructures are connected by trunks, open rails shall be fitted for the whole length of the exposed parts of the freeboard deck.

Chapter III
Freeboards

Regulation 27
Types of ships

(1)   For the purposes of freeboard computation ships shall be divided into type 'A' and type 'B'.

Type 'A' ships

(2)   A type 'A' ship is one which is designed to carry only liquid cargoes in bulk, and in which cargo tanks have only small access openings closed by watertight gasketed covers of steel or equivalent material. Such a ship necessarily has the following inherent features:

  (a) high integrity of the exposed deck; and

  (b) high degree of safety against flooding, resulting from the low permeability of loaded cargo spaces and the degree of subdivision usually provided.

(3)   A type 'A' ship if over 150 m (492 feet) in length, and designed to have empty compartments when loaded to her summer load waterline, shall be able to withstand the flooding of any one of these empty compartments at an assumed permeability of 0.95, and remain afloat in a condition of equilibrium considered to be satisfactory by the Administration. In such a ship, if over 225 m (738 feet) in length, the machinery space shall be treated as a floodable compartment but with a permeability of 0.85.

For the guidance of Administrations the following limits may be regarded as satisfactory:

  (a) The final waterline after flooding is below the lower edge of any opening through which progressive flooding may take place.

  (b) The maximum angle of heel due to unsymmetrical flooding is of the order of 15°.

  (c) The metacentric height in the flooded condition is positive.

(4)   A type 'A' ship shall be assigned a freeboard not less than that based on table A of regulation 28.

Type 'B' ships

(5)   All ships which do not come within the provisions regarding type 'A' ships in paragraphs (2) and (3) of this regulation shall be considered as type 'B' ships.

(6)   Type 'B' ships which in position 1 have hatchways fitted with hatch covers complying with the requirements of regulation 15(7) or 16 shall, except as provided in paragraphs (7) to (10) inclusive of this regulation, be assigned freeboards based on table B of regulation 28.

(7)   Any type 'B' ships of over 100 m (328 feet) in length may be assigned freeboards less than those required under paragraph (6) of this regulation provided that, in relation to the amount of reduction granted, the Administration is satisfied that:

(a)   the measures provided for the protection of the crew are adequate;

(b)   the freeing arrangements are adequate;

(c)   the covers in positions 1 and 2 comply with the provisions of regulation 16 and have adequate strength, special care being given to their sealing and securing arrangements;

---
see also the unified interpretation

(d)   the ship, when loaded to her summer load waterline, will remain afloat in a satisfactory condition of equilibrium after flooding of any single damaged compartment at an assumed permeability of 0.95 excluding the machinery space; and

(e)   in such a ship, over 225 m (738 feet) in length, the machinery space shall be treated as a floodable compartment but with a permeability of 0.85.

For the guidance of Administrations in applying sub-paragraphs (d) and (e) of this paragraph the limits given in sub-paragraphs (3) (a), (b) and (c) may be regarded as satisfactory.

The relevant calculations may be based upon the following main assumptions:

–   the vertical extent of damage is equal to the depth of the ship;

–   the penetration of damage is not more than $\dfrac{B}{5}$

–   no main transverse bulkhead is damaged;

–   the height of the centre of gravity above the base line is assessed allowing for homogeneous loading of cargo holds, and for 50% of the designed capacity of consumable fluids and stores, etc.

---
see also the unified interpretation
---

(8)   In calculating the freeboards for type 'B' ships which comply with the requirements of paragraph (7) of this regulation, the values from table B of regulation 28 shall not be reduced by more than 60% of the difference between the 'B' and 'A' tabular values for the appropriate ship lengths.

(9)   The reduction in tabular freeboard allowed under paragraph (8) of this regulation may be increased up to the total difference between the values in table A and those in table B of regulation 28 on condition that the ship complies with the requirements of regulation 26(1), (2), (3), (5) and (6), as if it were a type 'A' ship, and further complies with the provisions of paragraph 7 (a) to (d) inclusive of this regulation except that the reference in sub-paragraph (d) to the flooding of any single damaged compartment shall be treated as a reference to the flooding of any two adjacent fore and aft compartments, neither of which is the machinery space. Also any such ship of over 225 m (738 feet) in length, when loaded to her summer load waterline, shall remain afloat in a satisfactory condition of equilibrium after flooding of the machinery space, taken alone, at an assumed permeability of 0.85.

---
see also the unified interpretation
---

(10)   Type 'B' ships, which in position 1 have hatchways fitted with hatch covers which comply with the requirements of regulation 15, other than paragraph (7), shall be assigned freeboards based upon the values given in table B of regulation 28 increased by the values given in the following table:

Freeboard increase over tabular freeboard for type 'B' ships, for ships with hatch covers not complying with regulation 15(7) or 16

Length of ship (m)	Freeboard increase (mm)	Length of ship (m)	Freeboard increase (mm)	Length of ship (m)	Freeboard increase (mm)
108 and below	50	139	175	171	292
		140	181	172	294
109	52	141	186	173	297
110	55	142	191	174	299
111	57	143	196	175	301
112	59	144	201	176	304
113	62	145	206	177	306
114	64	146	210	178	308
115	68	147	215	179	311
116	70	148	219	180	313
117	73	149	224	181	315
118	76	150	228	182	318
119	80	151	232	183	320
120	84	152	236	184	322
121	87	153	240	185	325
122	91	154	244	186	327
123	95	155	247	187	329
124	99	156	251	188	332
125	103	157	254	189	334
126	108	158	258	190	336
127	112	159	261	191	339
128	116	160	264	192	341
129	121	161	267	193	343
130	126	162	270	194	346
131	131	163	273	195	348
132	136	164	275	196	350
133	142	165	278	197	353
134	147	166	280	198	355
135	153	167	283	199	357
136	159	168	285	200	358
137	164	169	287		
138	170	170	290		

Freeboards at intermediate lengths of ship shall be obtained by linear interpolation. Ships above 200 m in length shall be dealt with by the Administration.

Freeboard increase over tabular freeboard for type 'B' ships, for ships with hatch covers not complying with regulation 15(7) or 16

Length of ship (feet)	Freeboard increase (inches)	Length of ship (feet)	Freeboard increase (inches)
350 and below	2.0	510	9.6
		520	10.0
360	2.3	530	10.4
370	2.6	540	10.7
380	2.9	550	11.0
390	3.3	560	11.4
400	3.7	570	11.8
410	4.2	580	12.1
420	4.7	590	12.5
430	5.2	600	12.8
440	5.8	610	13.1
450	6.4	620	13.4
460	7.0	630	13.6
470	7.6	640	13.9
480	8.2	650	14.1
490	8.7	660	14.3
500	9.2		

Freeboards at intermediate lengths of ship shall be obtained by linear interpolation. Ship above 660 feet in length shall be dealt with by the Administration.

---
see also the unified interpretation
---

(11) A lighter, barge or other ship without independent means of propulsion shall be assigned a freeboard in accordance with the provisions of these regulations. However, in the case of barges which are unmanned the requirements of regulations 25, 26(2) and (3) and 39 shall not apply. Such unmanned barges which have on the freeboard deck only small access openings closed by weathertight gasketed covers of steel or equivalent material may be assigned freeboards 25% less than those calculated in accordance with these regulations.

---
see also the unified interpretations

Regulation 28
Freeboard tables

---
see also the unified interpretation

Type 'A' ships

(1) The tabular freeboard for type 'A' ships shall be determined from the following table:

41

Table A – *Freeboard table for type 'A' ships*

Length of ship (m)	Freeboard (mm)	Length of ship (m)	Freeboard (mm)	Length of ship (m)	Freeboard (mm)
24	200	69	693	114	1359
25	208	70	706	115	1376
26	217	71	720	116	1392
27	225	72	733	117	1409
28	233	73	746	118	1426
29	242	74	760	119	1442
30	250	75	773	120	1459
31	258	76	786	121	1476
32	267	77	800	122	1494
33	275	78	814	123	1511
34	283	79	828	124	1528
35	292	80	841	125	1546
36	300	81	855	126	1563
37	308	82	869	127	1580
38	316	83	883	128	1598
39	325	84	897	129	1615
40	334	85	911	130	1632
41	344	86	926	131	1650
42	354	87	940	132	1667
43	364	88	955	133	1684
44	374	89	969	134	1702
45	385	90	984	135	1719
46	396	91	999	136	1736
47	408	92	1014	137	1753
48	420	93	1029	138	1770
49	432	94	1044	139	1787
50	443	95	1059	140	1803
51	455	96	1074	141	1820
52	467	97	1089	142	1837
53	478	98	1105	143	1853
54	490	99	1120	144	1870
55	503	100	1135	145	1886
56	516	101	1151	146	1903
57	530	102	1166	147	1919
58	544	103	1181	148	1935
59	559	104	1196	149	1952
60	573	105	1212	150	1968
61	587	106	1228	151	1984
62	600	107	1244	152	2000
63	613	108	1260	153	2016
64	626	109	1276	154	2032
65	639	110	1293	155	2048
66	653	111	1309	156	2064
67	666	112	1326	157	2080
68	680	113	1342	158	2096

Table A *(continued)*

Length of ship (m)	Freeboard (mm)	Length of ship (m)	Freeboard (mm)	Length of ship (m)	Freeboard (mm)
159	2111	204	2650	249	3006
160	2126	205	2659	250	3012
161	2141	206	2669	251	3018
162	2155	207	2678	252	3024
163	2169	208	2687	253	3030
164	2184	209	2696	254	3036
165	2198	210	2705	255	3042
166	2212	211	2714	256	3048
167	2226	212	2723	257	3054
168	2240	213	2732	258	3060
169	2254	214	2741	259	3066
170	2268	215	2749	260	3072
171	2281	216	2758	261	3078
172	2294	217	2767	262	3084
173	2307	218	2775	263	3089
174	2320	219	2784	264	3095
175	2332	220	2792	265	3101
176	2345	221	2801	266	3106
177	2357	222	2809	267	3112
178	2369	223	2817	268	3117
179	2381	224	2825	269	3123
180	2393	225	2833	270	3128
181	2405	226	2841	271	3133
182	2416	227	2849	272	3138
183	2428	228	2857	273	3143
184	2440	229	2865	274	3148
185	2451	230	2872	275	3153
186	2463	231	2880	276	3158
187	2474	232	2888	277	3163
188	2486	233	2895	278	3167
189	2497	234	2903	279	3172
190	2508	235	2910	280	3176
191	2519	236	2918	281	3181
192	2530	237	2925	282	3185
193	2541	238	2932	283	3189
194	2552	239	2939	284	3194
195	2562	240	2946	285	3198
196	2572	241	2953	286	3202
197	2582	242	2959	287	3207
198	2592	243	2966	288	3211
199	2602	244	2973	289	3215
200	2612	245	2979	290	3220
201	2622	246	2986	291	3224
202	2632	247	2993	292	3228
203	2641	248	3000	293	3233

Table A *(continued)*

Length of ship (m)	Freeboard (mm)	Length of ship (m)	Freeboard (mm)	Length of ship (m)	Freeboard (mm)
294	3237	318	3325	342	3387
295	3241	319	3328	343	3389
296	3246	320	3331	344	3392
297	3250	321	3334	345	3394
298	3254	322	3337	346	3396
299	3258	323	3339	347	3399
300	3262	324	3342	348	3401
301	3266	325	3345	349	3403
302	3270	326	3347	350	3406
303	3274	327	3350	351	3408
304	3278	328	3353	352	3410
305	3281	329	3355	353	3412
306	3285	330	3358	354	3414
307	3288	331	3361	355	3416
308	3292	332	3363	356	3418
309	3295	333	3366	357	3420
310	3298	334	3368	358	3422
311	3302	335	3371	359	3423
312	3305	336	3373	360	3425
313	3308	337	3375	361	3427
314	3312	338	3378	362	3428
315	3315	339	3380	363	3430
316	3318	340	3382	364	3432
317	3322	341	3385	365	3433

Freeboards at intermediate lengths of ship shall be obtained by linear interpolation. Ships above 365 m in length shall be dealt with by the Administration.

Table A – *Freeboard table for type 'A' ships*

Length of ship (feet)	Freeboard (inches)	Length of ship (feet)	Freeboard (inches)	Length of ship (feet)	Freeboard (inches)
80	8.0	180	19.8	280	36.3
90	8.9	190	21.3	290	38.0
100	9.8	200	22.9	300	39.7
110	10.8	210	24.5	310	41.4
120	11.9	220	26.2	320	43.2
130	13.0	230	27.8	330	45.0
140	14.2	240	29.5	340	46.9
150	15.5	250	31.1	350	48.8
160	16.9	260	32.8	360	50.7
170	18.3	270	34.6	370	52.7

Table A *(continued)*

Length of ship (feet)	Freeboard (inches)	Length of ship (feet)	Freeboard (inches)	Length of ship (feet)	Freeboard (inches)
380	54.7	660	103.3	940	126.2
390	56.8	670	104.4	950	126.7
400	58.8	680	105.5	960	127.2
410	60.9	690	106.6	970	127.7
420	62.9	700	107.7	980	128.1
430	65.0	710	108.7	990	128.6
440	67.0	720	109.7	1000	129.0
450	69.1	730	110.7	1010	129.4
460	71.1	740	111.7	1020	129.9
470	73.1	750	112.6	1030	130.3
480	75.1	760	113.5	1040	130.7
490	77.1	770	114.4	1050	131.0
500	79.0	780	115.3	1060	131.4
510	80.9	790	116.1	1070	131.7
520	82.7	800	117.0	1080	132.0
530	84.5	810	117.8	1090	132.3
540	86.3	820	118.6	1100	132.6
550	88.0	830	119.3	1110	132.9
560	89.6	840	120.1	1120	133.2
570	91.1	850	120.7	1130	133.5
580	92.6	860	121.4	1140	133.8
590	94.1	870	122.1	1150	134.0
600	95.5	880	122.7	1160	134.3
610	96.9	890	123.4	1170	134.5
620	98.3	900	124.0	1180	134.7
630	99.6	910	124.6	1190	135.0
640	100.9	920	125.2	1200	135.2
650	102.1	930	125.7		

Freeboards at intermediate lengths of ship shall be obtained by linear interpolation. Ships above 1200 feet in length shall be dealt with by the Administration.

Type 'B' ships

(2) The tabular freeboard for type 'B' ships shall be determined from the following table:

Table B – *Freeboard table for type 'B' ships*

Length of ship (m)	Freeboard (mm)	Length of ship (m)	Freeboard (mm)	Length of ship (m)	Freeboard (mm)
24	200	28	233	32	267
25	208	29	242	33	275
26	217	30	250	34	283
27	225	31	258	35	292

Table B *(continued)*

Length of ship (m)	Freeboard (mm)	Length of ship (m)	Freeboard (mm)	Length of ship (m)	Freeboard (mm)
36	300	81	905	126	1815
37	308	82	923	127	1837
38	316	83	942	128	1859
39	325	84	960	129	1880
40	334	85	978	130	1901
41	344	86	996	131	1921
42	354	87	1015	132	1940
43	364	88	1034	133	1959
44	374	89	1054	134	1979
45	385	90	1075	135	2000
46	396	91	1096	136	2021
47	408	92	1116	137	2043
48	420	93	1135	138	2065
49	432	94	1154	139	2087
50	443	95	1172	140	2109
51	455	96	1190	141	2130
52	467	97	1209	142	2151
53	478	98	1229	143	2171
54	490	99	1250	144	2190
55	503	100	1271	145	2209
56	516	101	1293	146	2229
57	530	102	1315	147	2250
58	544	103	1337	148	2271
59	559	104	1359	149	2293
60	573	105	1380	150	2315
61	587	106	1401	151	2334
62	601	107	1421	152	2354
63	615	108	1440	153	2375
64	629	109	1459	154	2396
65	644	110	1479	155	2418
66	659	111	1500	156	2440
67	674	112	1521	157	2460
68	689	113	1543	158	2480
69	705	114	1565	159	2500
70	721	115	1587	160	2520
71	738	116	1609	161	2540
72	754	117	1630	162	2560
73	769	118	1651	163	2580
74	784	119	1671	164	2600
75	800	120	1690	165	2620
76	816	121	1709	166	2640
77	833	122	1729	167	2660
78	850	123	1750	168	2680
79	868	124	1771	169	2698
80	887	125	1793	170	2716

Table B *(continued)*

Length of ship (m)	Freeboard (mm)	Length of ship (m)	Freeboard (mm)	Length of Ship (m)	Freeboard (mm)
171	2735	216	3520	261	4165
172	2754	217	3537	262	4177
173	2774	218	3554	263	4189
174	2795	219	3570	264	4201
175	2815	220	3586	265	4214
176	2835	221	3601	266	4227
177	2855	222	3615	267	4240
178	2875	223	3630	268	4252
179	2895	224	3645	269	4264
180	2915	225	3660	270	4276
181	2933	226	3675	271	4289
182	2952	227	3690	272	4302
183	2970	228	3705	273	4315
184	2988	229	3720	274	4327
185	3007	230	3735	275	4339
186	3025	231	3750	276	4350
187	3044	232	3765	277	4362
188	3062	233	3780	278	4373
189	3080	234	3795	279	4385
190	3098	235	3808	280	4397
191	3116	236	3821	281	4408
192	3134	237	3835	282	4420
193	3151	238	3849	283	4432
194	3167	239	3864	284	4443
195	3185	240	3880	285	4455
196	3202	241	3893	286	4467
197	3219	242	3906	287	4478
198	3235	243	3920	288	4490
199	3249	244	3934	289	4502
200	3264	245	3949	290	4513
201	3280	246	3965	291	4525
202	3296	247	3978	292	4537
203	3313	248	3992	293	4548
204	3330	249	4005	294	4560
205	3347	250	4018	295	4572
206	3363	251	4032	296	4583
207	3380	252	4045	297	4595
208	3397	253	4058	298	4607
209	3413	254	4072	299	4618
210	3430	255	4085	300	4630
211	3445	256	4098	301	4642
212	3460	257	4112	302	4654
213	3475	258	4125	303	4665
214	3490	259	4139	304	4676
215	3505	260	4152	305	4686

Table B *(continued)*

Length of Ship (m)	Freeboard (mm)	Length of Ship (m)	Freeboard (mm)	Length of Ship (m)	Freeboard (mm)
306	4695	326	4909	346	5119
307	4704	327	4920	347	5130
308	4714	328	4931	348	5140
309	4725	329	4943	349	5150
310	4736	330	4955	350	5160
311	4748	331	4965	351	5170
312	4757	332	4975	352	5180
313	4768	333	4985	353	5190
314	4779	334	4995	354	5200
315	4790	335	5005	355	5210
316	4801	336	5015	356	5220
317	4812	337	5025	357	5230
318	4823	338	5035	358	5240
319	4834	339	5045	359	5250
320	4844	340	5055	360	5260
321	4855	341	5065	361	5268
322	4866	342	5075	362	5276
323	4878	343	5086	363	5285
324	4890	344	5097	364	5294
325	4899	345	5108	365	5303

Freeboards at intermediate lengths of ship shall be obtained by linear interpolation. Ships above 365 m in length shall be dealt with by the Administration.

Table B – *Freeboard table for type 'B' ships*

Length of ship (feet)	Freeboard (inches)	Length of ship (feet)	Freeboard (inches)	Length of ship (feet)	Freeboard (inches)
80	8.0	240	30.4	400	68.2
90	8.9	250	32.4	410	70.7
100	9.8	260	34.4	420	73.2
110	10.8	270	36.5	430	75.7
120	11.9	280	38.7	440	78.2
130	13.0	290	41.0	450	80.7
140	14.2	300	43.3	460	83.1
150	15.5	310	45.7	470	85.6
160	16.9	320	48.2	480	88.1
170	18.3	330	50.7	490	90.6
180	19.8	340	53.2	500	93.1
190	21.3	350	55.7	510	95.6
200	22.9	360	58.2	520	98.1
210	24.7	370	60.7	530	100.6
220	26.6	380	63.2	540	103.0
230	28.5	390	65.7	550	105.4

Table B *(continued)*

Length of ship (feet)	Freeboard (inches)	Length of ship (feet)	Freeboard (inches)	Length of ship (feet)	Freeboard (inches)
560	107.7	780	151.5	1000	184.4
570	110.0	790	153.2	1010	185.8
580	112.3	800	154.8	1020	187.2
590	114.6	810	156.4	1030	188.5
600	116.8	820	158.0	1040	189.8
610	119.0	830	159.6	1050	191.0
620	121.1	840	161.2	1060	192.3
630	123.2	850	162.8	1070	193.5
640	125.3	860	164.3	1080	194.8
650	127.3	870	165.9	1090	196.1
660	129.3	880	167.4	1100	197.3
670	131.3	890	168.9	1110	198.6
680	133.3	900	170.4	1120	199.9
690	135.3	910	171.8	1130	201.2
700	137.1	920	173.3	1140	202.3
710	139.0	930	174.7	1150	203.5
720	140.9	940	176.1	1160	204.6
730	142.7	950	177.5	1170	205.8
740	144.5	960	178.9	1180	206.9
750	146.3	970	180.3	1190	208.1
760	148.1	980	181.7	1200	209.3
770	149.8	990	183.1		

Freeboards at intermediate lengths of ship shall be obtained by linear interpolation. Ships above 1200 feet in length shall be dealt with by the Administration.

Regulation 29
*Correction to the freeboard for ships
under 100 m (328 feet) in length*

---
see also the unified interpretation

The tabular freeboard for a type 'B' ship of between 24 m (79 feet) and 100 m (328 feet) in length having enclosed superstructures with an effective length of up to 35% of the length of the ship shall be increased by:

$$7.5 \, (100 - L) \, (0.35 - \frac{E}{L}) \text{ mm}$$

where L = length of ship in metres,

> E = effective length of superstructure in metres as defined in regulation 35

49

or

$$0.09 \, (328 - L) \, (0.35 - \frac{E}{L}) \text{ inches}$$

where L = length of ship in feet

E = effective length of superstructure in feet as defined in regulation 35.

Regulation 30
Correction for block coefficient

Where the block coefficient (C_b) exceeds 0.68, the tabular freeboard specified in regulation 28 as modified, if applicable, by regulations 27(8), 27(10) and 29 shall be multiplied by the factor $\dfrac{C_b + 0.68}{1.36}$.

Regulation 31
Correction for depth

---
see also the unified interpretation

---

(1)   Where D exceeds $\dfrac{L}{15}$ the freeboard shall be increased by $(D - \dfrac{L}{15})R$ mm, where R is $\dfrac{L}{0.48}$ at lengths less than 120 m and 250 at 120 m length and above, or $(D - \dfrac{L}{15})R$ inches, where R is $\dfrac{L}{131.2}$ at lengths less than 393.6 feet and 3 at 393.6 feet length and above.

(2)   Where D is less than $\dfrac{L}{15}$ no reduction shall be made except in a ship with an enclosed superstructure covering at least 0.6L amidships, with a complete trunk, or combination of detached enclosed superstructures and trunks which extend all fore and aft, where the freeboard shall be reduced at the rate prescribed in paragraph (1) of this regulation.

(3)   Where the height of superstructure or trunk is less than the standard height, the reduction shall be in the ratio of the actual to the standard height as defined in regulation 33.

---
see also the unified interpretation

Regulation 32
Correction for position of deck line

Where the actual depth to the upper edge of the deck line is greater or less than D, the difference between the depths shall be added to or deducted from the freeboard.

Regulation 33
Standard height of superstructure

The standard height of a superstructure shall be as given in the following table:

	Standard height (m)	
L (m)	Raised quarter-deck	All other superstructures
30 or less	0.90	1.80
75	1.20	1.80
125 or more	1.80	2.30

	Standard height (feet)	
L (feet)	Raised quarter-deck	All other superstructures
98.5 or less	3.0	5.9
246	3.9	5.9
410 or more	5.9	7.5

The standard heights at intermediate lengths of the ship shall be obtained by linear interpolation.

Regulation 34
Length of superstructure

see also the unified interpretation

(1) Except as provided in paragraph (2) of this regulation, the length of a superstructure (S) shall be the mean length of the parts of the superstructure which lie within the length (L).

see also the unified interpretation

(2) Where the end bulkhead of an enclosed superstructure extends in a fair convex curve beyond its intersection with the superstructure sides, the length of the superstructure may be increased on the basis of an equivalent plane bulkhead. This increase shall be two-thirds of the fore and aft extent of the curvature. The maximum curvature which may be taken into account in determining this increase is one-half the breadth of the superstructure at the point of intersection of the curved end of the superstructure with its side.

see also the unified interpretation

Regulation 35
Effective length of superstructure

see also the unified interpretations

(1) Except as provided for in paragraph (2) of this regulation, the effective length (E) of an enclosed superstructure of standard height shall be its length.

(2) In all cases where an enclosed superstructure of standard height is set in from the sides of the ship as permitted in regulation 3(10), the effective length shall be the length modified by the ratio of b/B_s, where

    b is the breadth of the superstructure at the middle of its length; and

    B_s is the breadth of the ship at the middle of the length of the superstructure.

Where a superstructure is set in for a part of its length, this modification shall be applied only to the set-in part.

(3) Where the height of an enclosed superstructure is less than the standard height, the effective length shall be its length reduced in the ratio of the actual height to the standard height. Where the height exceeds the standard, no increase shall be made to the effective length of the superstructure.

see also the unified interpretation

(4) The effective length of a raised quarter-deck, if fitted with an intact front bulkhead, shall be its length up to a maximum of 0.6L. Where the bulkhead is not intact, the raised quarter-deck shall be treated as a poop of less than standard height.

see also the unified interpretations

(5) Superstructures which are not enclosed shall have no effective length.

Regulation 36
Trunks

see also the unified interpretations

(1) A trunk or similar structure which does not extend to the sides of the ship shall be regarded as efficient on the following conditions:

   (a) the trunk is at least as strong as a superstructure;

   (b) the hatchways are in the trunk deck, and the hatchway coamings and covers comply with the requirements of regulations 13 to 16 inclusive and the width of the trunk deck stringer provides a satisfactory gangway and sufficient lateral stiffness. However, small access openings with watertight covers may be permitted in the freeboard deck;

   (c) a permanent working platform fore and aft fitted with guard rails is provided by the trunk deck, or by detached trunks connected to superstructures by efficient permanent gangways;

   (d) ventilators are protected by the trunk, by watertight covers or by other equivalent means;

(e) open rails are fitted on the weather parts of the freeboard deck in way of the trunk for at least half their length;

<u>**see also the unified interpretation**</u>

(f) the machinery casings are protected by the trunk, by a super-structure of at least standard height, or by a deckhouse of the same height and of equivalent strength;

(g) the breadth of the trunk is at least 60% of the breadth of the ship; and

(h) where there is no superstructure, the length of the trunk is at least 0.6*L*.

(2) The full length of an efficient trunk reduced in the ratio of its mean breadth to *B* shall be its effective length.

(3) The standard height of a trunk is the standard height of a superstructure other than a raised quarter-deck.

(4) Where the height of a trunk is less than the standard height, its effective length shall be reduced in the ratio of the actual to the standard height. Where the height of hatchway coamings on the trunk deck is less than that required under regulation 15(1), a reduction from the actual height of trunk shall be made which corresponds to the difference between the actual and the required height of coaming.

<u>**see also the unified interpretation**</u>

Regulation 37
Deduction for superstructures and trunks

<u>**see also the unified interpretation**</u>

(1) Where the effective length of superstructures and trunks is 1.0*L*, the deduction from the freeboard shall be 350 mm at 24 m length of ship, 860 mm at 85 m length, and 1070 mm at 122 m length and above (14 inches at 79 feet length of ship, 34 inches at 279 feet length, and 42 inches at 400 feet length and above); deductions at intermediate lengths shall be obtained by linear interpolation.

(2) Where the total effective length of superstructures and trunks is less than 1.0*L* the deduction shall be a percentage obtained from one of the following tables:

Percentage of deduction for type 'A' ships

	Total effective length of superstructures and trunks										
	0	0.1*L*	0.2*L*	0.3*L*	0.4*L*	0.5*L*	0.6*L*	0.7*L*	0.8*L*	0.9*L*	1.0*L*
Percentage of deduction for all types of superstructures	0	7	14	21	31	41	52	63	75.3	87.7	100

Percentages at intermediate lengths of superstructures shall be obtained by linear interpolation.

Percentage of deduction for type 'B' ships

	Line	Total effective length of superstructures and trunks										
		0	0.1L	0.2L	0.3L	0.4L	0.5L	0.6L	0.7L	0.8L	0.9L	1.0L
Ships with forecastle and without detached bridge	I	0	5	10	15	23.5	32	46	63	75.3	87.7	100
Ships with forecastle and detached bridge	II	0	6.3	12.7	19	27.5	36	46	63	75.3	87.7	100

Percentages at intermediate lengths of superstructures shall be obtained by linear interpolation.

(3) For ships of type 'B':

    (a) Where the effective length of a bridge is less than 0.2L, the percentages shall be obtained by linear interpolation between lines I and II.

    (b) Where the effective length of a forecastle is more than 0.4L, the percentages shall be obtained from line II.

    (c) Where the effective length of a forecastle is less than 0.07L, the above percentages shall be reduced by:

$$5 \times \frac{(0.07L - f)}{0.07L}$$

where f is the effective length of the forecastle.

Regulation 38
Sheer

---
see also the unified interpretation

General

(1) The sheer shall be measured from the deck at side to a line of reference drawn parallel to the keel through the sheer line amidships.

(2) In ships designed with a rake of keel, the sheer shall be measured in relation to a reference line drawn parallel to the design load waterline.

(3) In flush deck ships and in ships with detached superstructures the sheer shall be measured at the freeboard deck.

(4)   In ships with topsides of unusual form in which there is a step or break in the topsides, the sheer shall be considered in relation to the equivalent depth amidships.

(5)   In ships with a superstructure of standard height which extends over the whole length of the freeboard deck, the sheer shall be measured at the superstructure deck. Where the height exceeds the standard the least difference (Z) between the actual and standard heights shall be added to each end ordinate. Similarly, the intermediate ordinates at distances of $\frac{1}{6}L$ and $\frac{1}{3}L$ from each perpendicular shall be increased by $0.444Z$ and $0.111Z$ respectively.

---
see also the unified interpretation

---

(6)   Where the deck of an enclosed superstructure has at least the same sheer as the exposed freeboard deck, the sheer of the enclosed portion of the freeboard deck shall not be taken into account.

(7)   Where an enclosed poop or forecastle is of standard height with greater sheer than that of the freeboard deck, or is of more than standard height, an addition to the sheer of the freeboard deck shall be made as provided in paragraph (12) of this regulation.

---
see also the unified interpretations

Standard sheer profile

(8)   The ordinates of the standard sheer profile are given in the following table:

Standard sheer profile
(where L is in metres)

	Station	Ordinate (mm)	Factor
After half	After perpendicular	$25(\frac{L}{3} + 10)$	1
	$\frac{1}{6}L$ from A.P.	$11.1(\frac{L}{3} + 10)$	3
	$\frac{1}{3}L$ from A.P.	$2.8(\frac{L}{3} + 10)$	3
	Amidships	0	1
Forward half	Amidships	0	1
	$\frac{1}{3}L$ from F.P.	$5.6(\frac{L}{3} + 10)$	3
	$\frac{1}{6}L$ from F.P.	$22.2(\frac{L}{3} + 10)$	3
	Forward perpendicular	$50(\frac{L}{3} + 10)$	1

Standard sheer profile
(where L is in feet)

	Station	Ordinate (inches)	Factor
After half	After perpendicular	$0.1L + 10$	1
	$\frac{1}{6}L$ from A.P.	$0.0444L + 4.44$	3
	$\frac{1}{3}L$ from A.P.	$0.0111L + 1.11$	3
	Amidships	0	1
Forward half	Amidships	0	1
	$\frac{1}{3}L$ from F.P.	$0.0222L + 2.22$	3
	$\frac{1}{6}L$ from F.P.	$0.0888L + 8.88$	3
	Forward perpendicular	$0.2L + 20$	1

Measurement of variation from standard sheer profile

(9)   Where the sheer profile differs from the standard, the four ordinates of each profile in the forward or after half shall be multiplied by the appropriate factors given in the table of ordinates. The difference between the sums of the respective products and those of the standard divided by 8 measures the deficiency or excess of sheer in the forward or after half. The arithmetical mean of the excess or deficiency in the forward and after halves measures the excess or deficiency of sheer.

(10)   Where the after half of the sheer profile is greater than the standard and the forward half is less than the standard, no credit shall be allowed for the part in excess and deficiency only shall be measured.

(11)   Where the forward half of the sheer profile exceeds the standard, and the after portion of the sheer profile is not less than 75% of the standard, credit shall be allowed for the part in excess; where the after part is less than 50% of the standard no credit shall be given for the excess sheer forward. Where the after sheer is between 50% and 75% of the standard, intermediate allowances may be granted for excess sheer forward.

(12)   Where sheer credit is given for a poop or forecastle the following formula shall be used:

$$s = \frac{yL'}{3L}$$

where s = sheer credit, to be deducted from the deficiency or added to the excess of sheer,

y = difference between actual and standard height of superstructure at the end of sheer,

L' = mean enclosed length of poop or forecastle up to a maximum length of $0.5L$,

L = length of ship as defined in regulation 3(1) of this annex.

The above formula provides a curve in the form of a parabola tangent to the actual sheer curve at the freeboard deck and intersecting the end ordinate at a point below the superstructure deck a distance equal to the standard height of a superstructure. The superstructure deck shall not be less than standard height above this curve at any point. This curve shall be used in determining the sheer profile for forward and after halves of the ship.

see also the unified interpretations

Correction for variations from standard sheer profile

(13) The correction for sheer shall be the deficiency or excess of sheer (see paragraphs (9) to (11) inclusive of this regulation), multiplied by

$$0.75 - \frac{S}{2L}$$

where S is the total length of enclosed superstructures.

Addition for deficiency in sheer

(14) Where the sheer is less than the standard, the correction for deficiency in sheer (see paragraph (13) of this regulation) shall be added to the freeboard.

Deduction for excess sheer

(15) In ships where an enclosed superstructure covers $0.1L$ before and $0.1L$ abaft amidships, the correction for excess of sheer as calculated under the provisions of paragraph (13) of this regulation shall be deducted from the freeboard; in ships where no enclosed superstructure covers amidships, no deduction shall be made from the freeboard; where an enclosed superstructure covers less than $0.1L$ before and $0.1L$ abaft amidships, the deduction shall be obtained by linear interpolation. The maximum deduction for excess sheer shall be at the rate of 125 mm per 100 m of length ($1\frac{1}{2}$ inches per 100 feet of length).

see also the unified interpretation

Regulation 39
Minimum bow height

see also the unified interpretation

(1) The bow height defined as the vertical distance at the forward perpendicular between the waterline corresponding to the assigned summer freeboard and the designed trim and the top of the exposed deck at side shall be not less than:

for ships below 250 m in length,

$$56L(1 - \frac{L}{500}) \frac{1.36}{C_b + 0.68} \text{ mm;}$$

for ships of 250 m and above in length,

$$7000\frac{1.36}{C_b + 0.68} \text{ mm;}$$

where L is the length of the ship in metres,

C_b is the block coefficient which is to be taken as not less than 0.68

or,

for ships below 820 feet in length,

$$0.672L(1 - \frac{L}{1640}) \frac{1.36}{C_b + 0.68} \text{ inches;}$$

for ships of 820 feet and above in length,

$$275.6\frac{1.36}{C_b + 0.68} \text{ inches;}$$

where L is the length of the ship in feet,

C_b is the block coefficient which is to be taken as not less than 0.68

(2)   Where the bow height required in paragraph (1) of this regulation is obtained by sheer, the sheer shall extend for at least 15% of the length of the ship measured from the forward perpendicular. Where it is obtained by fitting a superstructure, such superstructure shall extend from the stem to a point at least $0.07L$ abaft the forward perpendicular, and it shall comply with the following requirements:

(a) for ships not over 100 m (328 feet) in length it shall be enclosed as defined in regulation 3(10), and

(b) for ships over 100 m (328 feet) in length it need not comply with regulation 3(10), but shall be fitted with closing appliances to the satisfaction of the Administration.

---
see also the unified interpretation
---

(3)   Ships which, to suit exceptional operational requirements, cannot meet the requirements of paragraphs (1) and (2) of this regulation may be given special consideration by the Administration.

Regulation 40
Minimum freeboards

---
see also the unified interpretation

Summer freeboard

(1) The minimum freeboard in summer shall be the freeboard derived from the tables in regulation 28 as modified by the corrections in regulations 27, as applicable, 29, 30, 31, 32, 37, 38 and, if applicable, 39.

---
see also the unified interpretation
---

(2) The freeboard in salt water, as calculated in accordance with paragraph (1) of this regulation, but without the correction for deck line, as provided by regulation 32, shall not be less than 50 mm (2 inches). For ships having in position 1 hatchways with covers which do not comply with the requirements of regulations 15(7), 16 or 26, the freeboard shall be not less than 150 mm (6 inches).

Tropical freeboard

(3) The minimum freeboard in the Tropical Zone shall be the freeboard obtained by a deduction from the summer freeboard of one forty-eighth of the summer draught measured from the top of the keel to the centre of the ring of the load line mark.

(4) The freeboard in salt water, as calculated in accordance with paragraph (1) of this regulation, but without the correction for deck line, as provided by regulation 32, shall not be less than 50 mm (2 inches). For ships having in position 1 hatchways with covers which do not comply with the requirements of regulations 15(7), 16 or 26, the freeboard shall be not less than 150 mm (6 inches).

Winter freeboard

(5) The minimum freeboard in winter shall be the freeboard obtained by an addition to the summer freeboard of one forty-eighth of summer draught, measured from the top of the keel to the centre of the ring of the load line mark.

Winter North Atlantic freeboard

(6) The minimum freeboard for ships of not more than 100 m (328 feet) in length which enter any part of the North Atlantic defined in regulation 52 (annex II) during the winter seasonal period shall be the winter freeboard plus 50 mm (2 inches). For other ships, the Winter North Atlantic freeboard shall be the winter freeboard.

Fresh water freeboard

(7)   The minimum freeboard in fresh water of unit density shall be obtained by deducting from the minimum freeboard in salt water:

$$\frac{\Delta}{40T} \text{ cm (inches)}$$

where Δ = displacement in salt water in tons at the summer load waterline

T = tons per centimetre (inch) immersion in salt water at the summer load waterline.

(8)   Where the displacement at the summer load waterline cannot be certified, the deduction shall be one forty-eighth of summer draught, measured from the top of the keel to the centre of the ring of the load line mark.

Chapter IV
Special requirements for ships assigned timber freeboards

Regulation 41
Application of this chapter

Regulations 42 to 45 inclusive apply only to ships to which timber load lines are assigned.

Regulation 42
Definitions

(1) *Timber deck cargo.* The term "timber deck cargo" means a cargo of timber carried on an uncovered part of a freeboard or superstructure deck. The term does not include wood pulp or similar cargo.

(2) *Timber load line.* A timber deck cargo may be regarded as giving a ship a certain additional buoyancy and a greater degree of protection against the sea. For that reason, ships carrying a timber deck cargo may be granted a reduction of freeboard calculated according to the provisions of regulation 45 and marked on the ship's side in accordance with the provisions of regulations 6(3) and (4). However, in order that such special freeboard may be granted and used, the timber deck cargo shall comply with certain conditions which are laid down in regulation 44, and the ship itself shall also comply with certain conditions relating to its construction which are set out in regulation 43.

Regulation 43
Construction of ship

Superstructure

(1) Ships shall have a forecastle of at least standard height and a length of at least $0.07L$. In addition, if the ship is less than 100 m (328 feet) in length, a poop of at least standard height, or a raised quarter-deck with either a deckhouse or a strong steel hood of at least the same total height shall be fitted aft.

Double bottom tanks

(2) Double bottom tanks where fitted within the midship half length of the ship shall have adequate watertight longitudinal subdivision.

Bulwarks

(3) The ship shall be fitted either with permanent bulwarks at least 1 m ($39\frac{1}{2}$ inches) in height, specially stiffened on the upper edge and supported by strong bulwark stays attached to the deck and provided with necessary freeing ports, or with efficient rails of the same height and of specially strong construction.

61

Regulation 44
Stowage

---
see also the unified interpretation

General

(1) Openings in the weather deck over which cargo is stowed shall be securely closed and battened down. The ventilators shall be efficiently protected.

(2) Timber deck cargo shall extend over at least the entire available length which is the total length of the well or wells between superstructures. Where there is no limiting superstructure at the after end, the timber shall extend at least to the after end of the aftermost hatchway. The timber shall be stowed as solidly as possible to at least the standard height of the superstructure.

(3) On a ship within a seasonal winter zone in winter, the height of the deck cargo above the weather deck shall not exceed one-third of the extreme breadth of the ship.

(4) The timber deck cargo shall be compactly stowed, lashed and secured. It shall not interfere in any way with the navigation and necessary work of the ship.

Uprights

(5) Uprights, when required by the nature of the timber, shall be of adequate strength considering the breadth of the ship; the spacing shall be suitable for the length and character of timber carried, but shall not exceed 3 m (9.8 feet). Strong angles or metal sockets or equally efficient means shall be provided for securing the uprights.

Lashings

(6) Timber deck cargo shall be effeciently secured throughout its length by independent over-all lashings spaced not more than 3 m (9.8 feet) apart. Eye plates for these lashings shall be efficiently attached to the sheer strake or to the deck stringer plate at intervals of not more than 3 m (9.8 feet). The distance from an end bulkhead of a superstructure to the first eye plate shall be not more than 2 m (6.6 feet). Eye plates and lashings shall be provided 0.6 m ($23\frac{1}{2}$ inches) and 1.5 m (4.9 feet) from the ends of timber deck cargoes where there is no bulkhead.

(7) Lashings shall be not less than 19 mm ($\frac{3}{4}$ inch) close link chain or flexible wire rope of equivalent strength, fitted with sliphooks and turnbuckles, which shall be accessible at all times. Wire rope lashings shall have a short length of long link chain to permit the length of lashings to be regulated.

(8) When timber is in lengths less than 3.6 m (11.8 feet) the spacing of the lashings shall be reduced or other suitable provisions made to suit the length of timber.

(9) All fittings required for securing the lashings shall be of strength corresponding to the strength of the lashings.

Stability

(10)   Provision shall be made for a safe margin of stability at all stages of the voyage, regard being given to additions of weight, such as those due to absorption of water and icing, and to losses of weight such as those due to consumption of fuel and stores.

Protection of crew, access to machinery spaces, etc.

(11)   In addition to the requirements of regulation 25(5) of this annex guard rails or lifelines not more than 33 cm (13 inches) apart vertically shall be provided on each side of the deck cargo to a height of at least 1 m ($39\frac{1}{2}$ inches) above the cargo.

Steering arrangements

(12)   Steering arrangements shall be effectively protected from damage by cargo and, as far as practicable, shall be accessible. Efficient provision shall be made for steering in the event of a breakdown in the main steering arrangements.

Regulation 45
Computation for freeboard

(1)   The minimum summer freeboards shall be computed in accordance with regulations 27(5), 27(6), 27(11), 28, 29, 30, 31, 32, 37 and 38, except that regulation 37 is modified by substituting the following percentages for those given in regulation 37:

	Total effective length of superstructures										
	0	0.1L	0.2L	0.3L	0.4L	0.5L	0.6L	0.7L	0.8L	0.9L	1.0L
Percentage of deduction for all types of superstructure	20	31	42	53	64	70	76	82	88	94	100

Percentages at intermediate lengths of superstructures shall be obtained by linear interpolation.

(2)   The Winter Timber Freeboard shall be obtained by adding to the Summer Timber Freeboard one thirty-sixth of the moulded summer timber draught.

---
see also the unified interpretation

---

(3)   The Winter North Atlantic Timber Freeboard shall be the same as the Winter North Atlantic Freeboard prescribed in regulation 40(6).

---
see also the unified interpretation

---

(4)   The Tropical Timber Freeboard shall be obtained by deducting from the Summer Timber Freeboard one forty-eighth of the moulded summer timber draught.

(5)   The Fresh Water Timber Freeboard shall be computed in accordance with regulation 40(7) based on the summer timber load waterline.

Annex II
Zones, areas and seasonal periods

The zones and areas in this annex are, in general, based on the following criteria:

SUMMER — not more than 10% winds of force 8 Beaufort (34 knots) or more.

TROPICAL — not more than 1% winds of force 8 Beaufort (34 knots) or more. Not more than one tropical storm in 10 years in an area of 5° square in any one separate calendar month.

In certain special areas, for practical reasons, some degree of relaxation has been found acceptable.

A chart is attached to this annex to illustrate the zones and areas defined below.

Regulation 46
Northern Winter Seasonal Zones and Area

(1)   North Atlantic Winter Seasonal Zones I and II

(a)   The North Atlantic Winter Seasonal Zone I lies within the meridian of longitude 50° W from the coast of Greenland to latitude 45° N, thence the parallel of latitude 45° N to longitude 15° W, thence the meridian of longitude 15° W to latitude 60° N, thence the parallel of latitude 60° N to the Greenwich Meridian, thence this meridian northwards.

Seasonal periods:

> WINTER: 16 October to 15 April
> SUMMER: 16 April to 15 October

(b)   The North Atlantic Winter Seasonal Zone II lies within the meridian of longitude 68°30′ W from the coast of the United States to latitude 40° N, thence the rhumb line to the point latitude 36° N, longitude 73° W, thence the parallel of latitude 36° N to longitude 25° W and thence the rhumb line to Cape Toriñana.

Excluded from this zone are the North Atlantic Winter Seasonal Zone I and the Baltic Sea bounded by the parallel of the latitude of The Skaw in the Skaggerak.

Seasonal periods:

> WINTER: 1 November to 31 March
> SUMMER: 1 April to 31 October

(2)   North Atlantic Winter Seasonal Area

The boundary of the North Atlantic Winter Seasonal Area is

> the meridian of longitude 68°30′ W from the coast of the United States to latitude 40° N, thence the rhumb line to the southernmost intersection of the meridian of longitude 61° W with the coast of Canada and thence the east coasts of Canada and the United States.

Seasonal periods:

For ships over 100 m (328 feet) in length:

> WINTER: 16 December to 15 February
> SUMMER: 16 February to 15 December

For ships of 100 m (328 feet) and under in length:

> WINTER: 1 November to 31 March
> SUMMER: 1 April to 31 October

(3)   North Pacific Winter Seasonal Zone

The southern boundary of the North Pacific Winter Seasonal Zone is

> the parallel of latitude 50° N from the east coast of the USSR to the west coast of Sakhalin, thence the west coast of Sakhalin to the southern extremity of Cape Kril'on, thence the rhumb line to Wakkanai, Hokkaido, Japan, thence the east and south coasts of Hokkaido to longitude 145° E, thence the meridian of longitude 145° E to latitude 35° N, thence the parallel of latitude 35° N to longitude 150° W and thence the rhumb line to the southern extremity of Dall Island, Alaska.

Seasonal periods:

> WINTER: 16 October to 15 April
> SUMMER: 16 April to 15 October

Regulation 47
Southern Winter Seasonal Zone

The northern boundary of the Southern Winter Seasonal Zone is

> the rhumb line from the east coast of the American continent at Cape Tres Puntas to the point latitude 34° S, longitude 50° W, thence the parallel of latitude 34° S to longitude 17° E, thence the rhumb line to the point latitude 35°10′ S, longitude 20° E, thence the rhumb line to the point latitude 34° S, longitude 28° E, thence along the rhumb line to the point latitude 35°30′ S, longitude 118° E, and thence the rhumb line to Cape Grim on the north-west coast of Tasmania; thence along the north and east coasts of Tasmania to the southernmost point of Bruny Island, thence the rhumb line to Black Rock Point on Stewart Island, thence the rhumb line to the point latitude 47° S, longitude

170° E, thence along the rhumb line to the point latitude 33° S, longitude 170° W, and thence the parallel of latitude 33° S to the west coast of the American continent.

Seasonal periods:

WINTER: 16 April to 15 October
SUMMER: 16 October to 15 April

Regulation 48
Tropical Zone
(1)   Northern boundary of the Tropical Zone

The northern boundary of the Tropical Zone is

the parallel of latitude 13° N from the east coast of the American continent to longitude 60° W, thence the rhumb line to the point latitude 10° N, longitude 58° W, thence the parallel of latitude 10° N to longitude 20° W, thence the meridian of longitude 20° W to latitude 30° N and thence the parallel of latitude 30° N to the west coast of Africa; from the east coast of Africa the parallel of latitude 8° N to longitude 70° E, thence the meridian of longitude 70° E to latitude 13° N, thence the parallel of latitude 13° N to the west coast of India; thence the south coast of India to latitude 10°30′ N on the east coast of India, thence the rhumb line to the point latitude 9° N, longitude 82° E, thence the meridian of longitude 82° E to latitude 8° N, thence the parallel of latitude 8° N to the west coast of Malaysia, thence the coast of South-East Asia to the east coast of Viet Nam at latitude 10° N, thence the parallel of latitude 10° N to longitude 145° E, thence the meridian of longitude 145° E to latitude 13° N and thence the parallel of latitude 13° N to the west coast of the American continent.

Saigon is to be considered as being on the boundary line of the Tropical Zone and the Seasonal Tropical Area.

(2)   Southern boundary of the Tropical Zone

The southern boundary of the Tropical Zone is

the rhumb line from the Port of Santos, Brazil, to the point where the meridian of longitude 40° W intersects the Tropic of Capricorn; thence the Tropic of Capricorn to the west coast of Africa; from the east coast of Africa the parallel of latitude 20° S to the west coast of Madagascar, thence the west and north coasts of Madagascar to longitude 50° E, thence the meridian of longitude 50° E to latitude 10° S, thence the parallel of latitude 10° S to longitude 98° E, thence the rhumb line to Port Darwin, Australia, thence the coasts of Australia and Wessel Island eastwards to Cape Wessel, thence the parallel of latitude 11° S to the west side of Cape York; from the east side of Cape York the parallel of latitude 11° S to longitude 150° W, thence the rhumb line to the point latitude 26° S, longitude 75° W, and thence the rhumb line to the west coast of the American continent at latitude 30° S.

Coquimbo and Santos are to be considered as being on the boundary line of the Tropical and Summer Zones.

(3)   Areas to be included in the Tropical Zone

The following areas are to be treated as included in the Tropical Zone:

(a) The Suez Canal, the Red Sea and the Gulf of Aden, from Port Said to the meridian of longitude 45° E.

Aden and Berbera are to be considered as being on the boundary line of the Tropical Zone and the Seasonal Tropical Area.

(b) The Persian Gulf to the meridian of longitude 59° E.

(c) The area bounded by the parallel of latitude 22° S from the east coast of Australia to the Great Barrier Reef, thence the Great Barrier Reef to latitude 11° S. The northern boundary of the area is the southern boundary of the Tropical Zone.

Regulation 49
Seasonal tropical areas

The following are Seasonal Tropical Areas:

(1)   In the North Atlantic
An area bounded

on the north by the rhumb line from Cape Catoche, Yucatan, to Cape San Antonio, Cuba, the north coast of Cuba to latitude 20° N and thence the parallel of latitude 20° N to longitude 20° W;

on the west by the coast of the American continent;

on the south and east by the northern boundary of the Tropical Zone.

Seasonal periods:

TROPICAL: 1 November to 15 July
SUMMER: 16 July to 31 October

(2)   In the Arabian Sea
An area bounded

on the west by the coast of Africa, the meridian of longitude 45° E in the Gulf of Aden, the coast of South Arabia and the meridian of longitude 59° E in the Gulf of Oman;

on the north and east by the coasts of Pakistan and India;

on the south by the northern boundary of the Tropical Zone.

Seasonal periods:

TROPICAL: 1 September to 31 May
SUMMER: 1 June to 31 August

(3)   In the Bay of Bengal

The Bay of Bengal north of the northern boundary of the Tropical Zone.

Seasonal periods:

TROPICAL: 1 December to 30 April
SUMMER: 1 May to 30 November

(4)   In the South Indian Ocean

(a)   An area bounded

on the north and west by the southern boundary of the Tropical Zone and the east coast of Madagascar;

on the south by the parallel of latitude 20° S;

on the east by the rhumb line from the point latitude 20° S, longitude 50° E, to the point latitude 15° S, longitude 51°30′ E, and thence by the meridian of longitude 51°30′ E to latitude 10° S.

Seasonal periods:

TROPICAL: 1 April to 30 November
SUMMER: 1 December to 31 March

(b)   An area bounded

on the north by the southern boundary of the Tropical Zone;

on the east by the coast of Australia;

on the south by the parallel of latitude 15° S from longitude 51°30′ E to longitude 120° E and thence the meridian of longitude 120° E to the coast of Australia;

on the west by the meridian of longitude 51°30′ E.

Seasonal periods:

TROPICAL: 1 May to 30 November
SUMMER: 1 December to 30 April

(5)   In the China Sea

An area bounded

on the west and north by the coasts of Viet Nam and China from latitude 10° N to Hong Kong;

on the east by the rhumb line from Hong Kong to the Port of Sual (Luzon Island) and the west coasts of the Islands of Luzon, Samar, and Leyte to latitude 10° N;

on the south by the parallel of latitude 10° N.

Hong Kong and Sual are to be considered as being on the boundary of the Seasonal Tropical Area and Summer Zone.

Seasonal periods:

TROPICAL: 21 January to 30 April
SUMMER: 1 May to 20 January

(6)   In the North Pacific

(a)   An area bounded

on the north by the parallel of latitude 25° N;

on the west by the meridian of longitude 160° E;

on the south by the parallel of latitude 13° N;

on the east by the meridian of longitude 130° W.

Seasonal periods:

TROPICAL: 1 April to 31 October
SUMMER: 1 November to 31 March

(b)   An area bounded

on the north and east by the west coast of the American continent;

on the west by the meridian of longitude 123° W from the coast of the American continent to latitude 33° N and by the rhumb line from the point latitude 33° N, longitude 123° W, to the point latitude 13° N, longitude 105° W;

on the south by the parallel of latitude 13° N.

Seasonal periods:

TROPICAL: 1 March to 30 June and 1 November to 30 November
SUMMER: 1 July to 31 October and 1 December to 28/29 February.

(7)   In the South Pacific

(a)   The Gulf of Carpentaria south of latitude 11° S.

Seasonal periods:

TROPICAL: 1 April to 30 November
SUMMER: 1 December to 31 March

(b)   An area bounded

on the north and east by the southern boundary of the Tropical Zone;

on the south by the Tropic of Capricorn from the east coast of Australia to longitude 150° W, thence by the meridian of longitude 150° W to latitude 20° S and thence by the parallel of latitude 20° S to the point where it intersects the southern boundary of the Tropical Zone;

on the west by the boundaries of the area within the Great Barrier Reef included in the Tropical Zone and by the east coast of Australia.

Seasonal periods:

TROPICAL: 1 April to 30 November
SUMMER: 1 December to 31 March

Regulation 50
Summer Zones

The remaining areas constitute the Summer Zones.

However, for ships of 100 m (328 feet) and under in length, the area bounded

    on the north and west by the east coast of the United States;

    on the east by the meridian of longitude 68°30′ W from the coast of the United States to latitude 40° N and thence by the rhumb line to the point latitude 36° N, longitude 73° W;

    on the south by the parallel of latitude 36° N

is a Winter Seasonal Area.

Seasonal periods:

    WINTER: 1 November to 31 March
    SUMMER: 1 April to 31 October

Regulation 51
Enclosed seas

(1)   Baltic Sea

This sea bounded by the parallel of latitude of The Skaw in the Skagerrak is included in the Summer Zones.

However, for ships of 100 m (328 feet) and under in length, it is a Winter Seasonal Area.

Seasonal periods:

    WINTER: 1 November to 31 March
    SUMMER: 1 April to 31 October

(2)   Black Sea

This sea is included in the Summer Zones.

However, for ships of 100 m (328 feet) and under in length, the area north of latitude 44° N is a Winter Seasonal Area.

Seasonal periods:

    WINTER: 1 December to 28/29 February
    SUMMER: 1 March to 30 November

(3)   Mediterranean

This sea is included in the Summer Zones.

However, for ships of 100 m (328 feet) and under in length, the area bounded

    on the north and west by the coasts of France and Spain and the meridian of longitude 3° E from the coast of Spain to latitude 40° N;

on the south by the parallel of latitude 40° N from longitude 3° E to the west coast of Sardinia;

on the east by the west and north coasts of Sardinia from latitude 40° N to longitude 9° E, thence by the meridian of longitude 9° E to the south coast of Corsica, thence by the west and north coasts of Corsica to longitude 9° E and thence by the rhumb line to Cape Sicié

is a Winter Seasonal Area.

Seasonal periods:

> WINTER: 16 December to 15 March
> SUMMER: 16 March to 15 December

(4)   Sea of Japan

This sea south of latitude 50° N is included in the Summer Zones.

However, for ships of 100 m (328 feet) and under in length, the area between the parallel of latitude 50° N and the rhumb line from the east coast of Korea at latitude 38° N to the west coast of Hokkaido, Japan, at latitude 43°12′ N is a Winter Seasonal Area.

Seasonal periods:

> WINTER: 1 December to 28/29 February
> SUMMER: 1 March to 30 November

Regulation 52
The Winter North Atlantic Load Line

The part of the North Atlantic referred to in regulation 40(6) (annex I) comprises:

(a)   that part of the North Atlantic Winter Seasonal Zone II which lies between the meridians of 15° W and 50° W;

(b)   the whole of the North Atlantic Winter Seasonal Zone I, the Shetland Islands to be considered as being on the boundary.

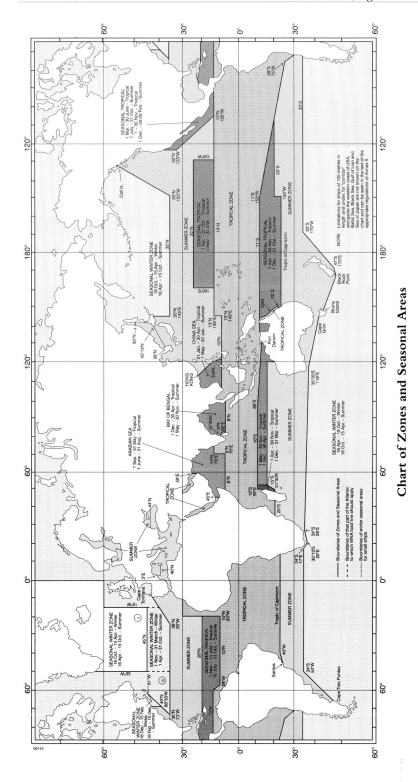

Chart of Zones and Seasonal Areas

73

Annex III
Certificates

INTERNATIONAL LOAD LINE CERTIFICATE (1966)

(Official seal)

Issued under the provisions of the International Convention on Load Lines, 1966, under the authority of the government of

_____

(full official designation of the country)

by   _____

*(full official designation of the competent person
or organization recognized under the provisions
of the International Convention on Load Lines, 1966)*

Name of ship	Distinctive number or letters	Port of registry	Length (*L*) as defined in article 2(8)

Freeboard assigned as: Type of ship

* { A new ship

An existing ship

* { Type 'A'
Type 'B'
Type 'B' with reduced freeboard
Type 'B' with increased freeboard

_____

* Delete whatever is inapplicable.

Freeboard from deck line		Load line
Tropical	. . . . mm (inches) (T)	. . . . mm (inches) above (S)
Summer	. . . . mm (inches) (S)	Upper edge of line through centre of ring
Winter	. . . . mm (inches) (W)	. . . . mm (inches) below (S)
Winter North Atlantic	. . . . mm (inches) (WNA)	. . . . mm (inches) below (S)
Timber tropical	. . . . mm (inches) (LT)	. . . . mm (inches) above (LS)
Timber summer	. . . . mm (inches) (LS)	. . . . mm (inches) above (S)
Timber winter	. . . . mm (inches) (LW)	. . . . mm (inches) below (LS)
Timber winter North Atlantic	. . . . mm (inches) (LWNA)	. . . . mm (inches) below (LS)

NOTE: Freeboards and load lines which are not applicable need not be entered on the certificate.

Allowance for fresh water for all freeboards other than timber . . . . mm (inches). For timber freeboards . . . . mm (inches).

The upper edge of the deck line from which these freeboards are measured is . . . . mm (inches) . . . . deck at side.

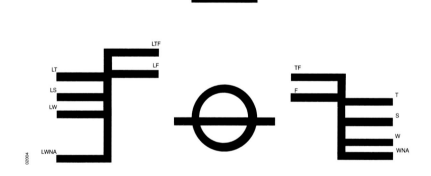

Date of initial or periodical survey . . . .

This is to certify that this ship has been surveyed and that the freeboards have been assigned and load lines shown above have been marked in accordance with the International Convention on Load Lines, 1966

This certificate is valid until . . . ., subject to periodical inspections in accordance with article 14(1)(c) of the Convention.

Issued at . . . .
(Place of issue of certificate)

. . . . 19 . . .   .
(Date of issue)   *(Signature of official issuing the certificate)*
and/or
(Seal of issuing authority)

If signed, the following paragraph is to be added:

The undersigned declares that he is duly authorized by the said Government to issue this certificate.

. . . .
(signature)

NOTES: 1 When a ship departs from a port situated on a river or inland waters, deeper loading shall be permitted corresponding to the weight of fuel and all other materials required for consumption between the point of departure and the sea.

2 When a ship is in fresh water of unit density the appropriate load line may be submerged by the amount of fresh water allowance shown above. Where the density is other than unity, an allowance shall be made proportional to the difference between 1.025 and the actual density.

Reverse of Certificate

THIS IS TO CERTIFY that at a periodical inspection required by article 14(1)(c) of the Convention, the ship was found to comply with the relevant provisions of the Convention.

Place . . . .   Date . . . .

signature and/or seal of issuing authority

Place . . . .   Date . . . .

signature and/or seal of issuing authority

Place . . . .   Date . . . .

signature and/or seal of issuing authority

Place . . . .   Date . . . .

signature and/or seal of issuing authority

The provisions of the Convention being fully complied with by this ship, the validity of this certificate is, in accordance with article 19(2) of the Convention, extended until
. . . .

Place . . . .   Date . . . .

signature and/or seal of issuing authority

INTERNATIONAL LOAD LINE EXEMPTION CERTIFICATE

(Official seal)

Issued under the provisions of the International Convention on Load Lines, 1966, under the authority of the government of

_____

(full official designation of the country)

by   _____

*(full official designation of the competent person
or organization recognized under the provisions
of the International Convention on Load Lines, 1966)*

Name of ship	Distinctive number or letters	Port of registry

This is to certify that the above-mentioned ship is exempted from the provisions of the 1966 Convention, under the authority conferred by article 6(2)/article 6(4)* of the Convention referred to above.

The provisions of the Convention from which the ship is exempted under article 6(2) are:

. . . .

. . . .

. . . .

The voyage for which exemption is granted under article 6(4) is:

From: . . . .

To: . . . .

_____

* Delete whichever is inapplicable.

Conditions, if any, on which the exemption is granted under either article 6(2) or article 6(4):

. . . .

. . . .

. . . .

This certificate is valid until . . . . subject, where appropriate, to periodical inspections in accordance with article 14(1)(c) of the Convention.

Issued at . . . .
(Place of issue of certificate)

. . . . 19 . . .   .
(Date of issue)   *(Signature of official issuing the certificate)*
                                                     and/or
                                          (Seal of issuing authority)

If signed, the following paragraph is to be added:

The undersigned declares that he is duly authorized by the said Government to issue this certificate.

. . . .
(Signature)

Reverse of Certificate

This is to certify that this ship continues to comply with the conditions under which this exemption was granted.

Place . . . .   Date . . . .

signature and/or seal of issuing authority

Place . . . .   Date . . . .

signature and/or seal of issuing authority

Place . . . .   Date . . . .

signature and/or seal of issuing authority

Place . . . .   Date . . . .

signature and/or seal of issuing authority

This ship continues to comply with the conditions under which this exemption was granted and the validity of this certificate is, in accordance with article 19(4)(a) of the Convention, extended until . . . .

Place . . . .   Date . . . .

signature and/or seal of issuing authority

81

Part 2
Articles of the Protocol of 1988 relating to the International Convention on Load Lines, 1966

Protocol of 1988 relating to the International Convention on Load Lines, 1966

THE PARTIES TO THE PRESENT PROTOCOL,

BEING PARTIES to the International Convention on Load Lines, 1966, done at London on 5 April 1966,

RECOGNIZING the significant contribution which is made by the above-mentioned Convention to the promotion of the safety of ships and property at sea and the lives of persons on board,

RECOGNIZING ALSO the need to improve further the technical provisions of the above-mentioned Convention,

RECOGNIZING FURTHER the need for the introduction into the above-mentioned Convention of provisions for survey and certification harmonized with corresponding provisions in other international instruments,

CONSIDERING that these needs may best be met by the conclusion of a Protocol relating to the International Convention on Load Lines, 1966,

HAVE AGREED as follows:

Article I
General obligations

1   The Parties to the present Protocol undertake to give effect to the provisions of the present Protocol and the Annexes hereto, which shall constitute an integral part of the present Protocol. Every reference to the present Protocol constitutes at the same time a reference to the Annexes hereto.

2   As between the Parties to the present Protocol, the provisions of the International Convention on Load Lines, 1966 (hereinafter referred to as "the Convention"), except article 29, shall apply subject to the modifications and additions set out in the present Protocol.

3   With respect to ships entitled to fly the flag of a State which is not a Party to the Convention and the present Protocol, the Parties to the present Protocol shall apply the requirements of the Convention and the present Protocol as may be necessary to ensure that no more favourable treatment is given to such ships.

Article II
Existing certificates

1   Notwithstanding any other provisions of the present Protocol, any International Load Line Certificate which is current when the present Protocol enters into force in respect of the Government of the State whose flag the ship is entitled to fly shall remain valid until it expires.

2 A Party to the present Protocol shall not issue certificates under, and in accordance with, the provisions of the International Convention on Load Lines, 1966, as adopted on 5 April 1966.

Article III
Communication of information

The Parties to the present Protocol undertake to communicate to, and deposit with, the Secretary-General of the International Maritime Organization (hereinafter referred to as "the Organization"):

(a) the text of laws, decrees, orders and regulations and other instruments which have been promulgated on the various matters within the scope of the present Protocol;

(b) a list of nominated surveyors or recognized organizations which are authorized to act on their behalf in the administration of load line matters for circulation to the Parties for information of their officers, and a notification of the specific responsibilities and conditions of the authority delegated to those nominated surveyors or recognized organizations; and

(c) a sufficient number of specimens of their certificates issued under the provisions of the present Protocol.

Article IV
Signature, ratification, acceptance, approval and accession

1 The present Protocol shall be open for signature at the Headquarters of the Organization from 1 March 1989 to 28 February 1990 and shall thereafter remain open for accession. Subject to the provisions of paragraph 3, States may express their consent to be bound by the present Protocol by:

(a) signature without reservation as to ratification, acceptance or approval; or

(b) signature subject to ratification, acceptance or approval, followed by ratification, acceptance or approval; or

(c) accession.

2 Ratification, acceptance, approval or accession shall be effected by the deposit of an instrument to that effect with the Secretary-General of the Organization.

3 The present Protocol may be signed without reservation, ratified, accepted, approved or acceded to only by States which have signed without reservation, accepted or acceded to the Convention.

Article V
Entry into force

1 The present Protocol shall enter into force twelve months after the date on which both the following conditions have been met:

(a) not less than fifteen States, the combined merchant fleets of which constitute not less than fifty per cent of the gross tonnage of the world's merchant shipping, have expressed their consent to be bound by it in accordance with article IV, and

(b) the conditions for the entry into force of the Protocol of 1988 relating to the International Convention for the Safety of Life at Sea, 1974 have been met,

provided that the present Protocol shall not enter into force before 1 February 1992.

2 For States which have deposited an instrument of ratification, acceptance, approval or accession in respect of the present Protocol after the conditions for entry into force thereof have been met but prior to the date of entry into force, the ratification, acceptance, approval or accession shall take effect on the date of entry into force of the present Protocol or three months after the date of deposit of the instrument, whichever is the later date.

3 Any instrument of ratification, acceptance, approval or accession deposited after the date on which the present Protocol enters into force shall take effect three months after the date of deposit.

4 After the date of which an amendment to the present Protocol or an amendment, as between the Parties to the present Protocol, to the Convention is deemed to have been accepted under article VI, any instrument of ratification, acceptance, approval or accession deposited shall apply to the present Protocol or the Convention as amended.

Article VI
Amendments

1 The present Protocol and, as between the Parties to the present Protocol, the Convention may be amended by either of the procedures specified in the following paragraphs.

2 Amendment after consideration within the Organization:

(a) Any amendment proposed by a Party to the present Protocol shall be submitted to the Secretary-General of the Organization, who shall then circulate it to all Members of the Organization and all Contracting Governments to the Convention at least six months prior to its consideration.

(b) Any amendment proposed and circulated as above shall be referred to the Maritime Safety Committee of the Organization for consideration.

(c) States which are Parties to the present Protocol, whether or not Members of the Organization, shall be entitled to participate in the proceedings of the Maritime Safety Committee for the consideration and adoption of amendments.

(d) Amendments shall be adopted by a two-thirds majority of the Parties to the present Protocol present and voting in the Maritime Safety Committee expanded as provided for in subparagraph (c) (hereinafter referred to as "the expanded Maritime Safety Committee") on condition that at least one third of the Parties shall be present at the time of voting.

(e) Amendments adopted in accordance with subparagraph (d) shall be communicated by the Secretary-General of the Organization to all Parties to the present Protocol for acceptance.

(f) (i) An amendment to an article or Annex A to the present Protocol or an amendment, as between Parties to the present Protocol, to an article of the Convention, shall be deemed to have been accepted on the date on which it is accepted by two thirds of the Parties to the present Protocol.

(ii) An amendment to Annex B to the present Protocol or an amendment, as between Parties to the present Protocol, to an Annex to the Convention, shall be deemed to have been accepted:

(aa) at the end of two years from the date on which it is communicated to Parties to the present Protocol for acceptance; or

(bb) at the end of a different period, which shall not be less than one year, if so determined at the time of its adoption by a two-thirds majority of the Parties present and voting in the expanded Maritime Safety Committee.

However, if within the specified period either more than one third of the Parties, or Parties the combined merchant fleets of which constitute not less than fifty per cent of the gross tonnage of all the merchant fleets of all Parties, notify the Secretary-General of the Organization that they object to the amendment, it shall be deemed not to have been accepted.

(g) (i) An amendment referred to in subparagraph (f)(i) shall enter into force with respect to those Parties to the present Protocol which have accepted it, six months after the date on which it is deemed to have been accepted, and with respect to each Party which accepts it after the date, six months after the date of that Party's acceptance.

(ii) An amendment referred to in subparagraph (f)(ii) shall enter into force with respect to all Parties to the present Protocol, except those which have objected to the amendment under that subparagraph and which have not withdrawn such objections, six months after the date on which it is deemed to have been accepted. However, before the date set for entry into force, any Party may give notice to the Secretary-General of the Organization that it exempts itself from giving effect to that amendment for a period not longer than one year from the date of its entry into force, or for such longer period as may be determined by a two-thirds majority of the Parties present and voting in the expanded Maritime Safety Committee at the time of the adoption of the amendment.

3   Amendment by a Conference:

(a)   Upon the request of a Party to the present Protocol concurred in by at least one third of the Parties, the Organization shall convene a Conference of Parties to consider amendments to the present Protocol and the Convention.

(b)   Every amendment adopted by such a Conference by a two-thirds majority of the Parties present and voting shall be communicated by the Secretary-General of the Organization to all Parties for acceptance.

(c)   Unless the Conference decides otherwise, the amendment shall be deemed to have been accepted and shall enter into force in accordance with the procedures specified in subparagraphs 2(f) and 2(g) respectively, provided that references in these paragraphs to the expanded Maritime Safety Committee shall be taken to mean references to the Conference.

4   (a)   A Party to the present Protocol which has accepted an amendment referred to in subparagraph 2(f)(ii) which has entered into force shall not be obliged to extend the benefit of the present Protocol in respect of the certificates issued to a ship entitled to fly the flag of a State Party which, pursuant to the provisions of that subparagraph, has objected to the amendment and has not withdrawn such an objection, in so far as such certificates relate to matters covered by the amendment in question.

(b)   A Party to the present Protocol which has accepted an amendment referred to in subparagraph 2(f)(ii) which has entered into force shall extend the benefit of the present Protocol in respect of the certificates issued to a ship entitled to fly the flag of a State Party which, pursuant to the provisions of subparagraph 2(g)(ii), has notified the Secretary-General of the Organization that it exempts itself from giving effect to the amendment.

5   Unless expressly provided otherwise, any amendment made under this article which relates to the structure of a ship shall apply only to ships the keels of which are laid or which are at a similar stage of construction on or after the date on which the amendment enters into force.

6   Any declaration of acceptance of, or objection to, an amendment or any notice given under subparagraph 2(g)(ii) shall be submitted in writing to the Secretary-General of the Organization, who shall inform all Parties to the present Protocol of any such submission and the date of its receipt.

7   The Secretary-General of the Organization shall inform all Parties to the present Protocol of any amendments which enter into force under this article, together with the date on which each such amendment enters into force.

Article VII
Denunciation

1   The present Protocol may be denounced by any Party at any time after the expiry of five years from the date on which the present Protocol enters into force for that Party.

2   Denunciation shall be effected by the deposit of an instrument of denunciation with the Secretary-General of the Organization.

3   A denunciation shall take effect one year or such longer period as may be specified in the instrument of denunciation, after its receipt by the Secretary-General of the Organization.

4   A denunciation of the Convention by a Party shall be deemed to be a denunciation of the present Protocol by that Party. Such denunciation shall take effect on the same date as denunciation of the Convention takes effect according to paragraph (3) of article 30 of the Convention.

Article VIII
Depositary

1   The present Protocol shall be deposited with the Secretary-General of the Organization (hereinafter referred to as "the depositary").

2   The depositary shall:

(a) inform the Governments of all States which have signed the present Protocol or acceded thereto of:

　(i) each new signature or deposit of an instrument of ratification, acceptance, approval or accession, together with the date thereof;

　(ii) the date of entry into force of the present Protocol;

　(iii) the deposit of any instrument of denunciation of the present Protocol together with the date on which it was received and the date on which the denunciation takes effect;

(b) transmit certified true copies of the present Protocol to the Governments of all States which have signed the present Protocol or acceded thereto.

3   As soon as the present Protocol enters into force, a certified true copy thereof shall be transmitted by the depositary to the Secretariat of the United Nations for registration and publication in accordance with Article 102 of the Charter of the United Nations.

Article IX
Languages

The present Protocol is established in a single original in the Arabic, Chinese, English, French, Russian and Spanish languages, each text being equally authentic.

DONE AT LONDON this eleventh day of November one thousand nine hundred and eighty-eight.

IN WITNESS WHEREOF the undersigned*, being duly authorized by their respective Governments for that purpose, have signed the present Protocol.

---

* Signatures omitted.

Part 3
Consolidated text of the International Convention on Load Lines, 1966 as modified by the Protocol of 1988 relating thereto, as amended

INTERNATIONAL CONVENTION
ON LOAD LINES, 1966
AS MODIFIED BY THE
1988 PROTOCOL RELATING THERETO,
AS AMENDED

Annex A
Articles of the
International Convention on Load Lines, 1966,
as modified by the Protocol of 1988
relating thereto

The Contracting Governments,

DESIRING to establish uniform principles and rules with respect to the limits to which ships on international voyages may be loaded having regard to the need for safeguarding life and property at sea;

CONSIDERING that this end may best be achieved by conclusion of a Convention;

HAVE AGREED as follows:

Article 1
General obligation under the Convention

(1) The Contracting Governments undertake to give effect to the provisions of the present Convention and the annexes hereto, which shall constitute an integral part of the present Convention. Every reference to the present Convention constitutes at the same time a reference to the annexes.

(2) The Contracting Governments shall undertake all measures which may be necessary to give effect to the present Convention.

Article 2
Definitions

For the purpose of the present Convention, unless expressly provided otherwise:

(1) *Regulations* means the regulations annexed to the present Convention.

(2) *Administration* means the Government of the State whose flag the ship is flying.

(3) *Approved* means approved by the Administration.

(4) *International voyage* means a sea voyage from a country to which the present Convention applies to a port outside such country, or conversely. For this purpose, every territory for the international relations of which a Contracting Government is responsible or for which the United Nations are the administering authority is regarded as a separate country.

(5) A *fishing vessel* is a ship used for catching fish, whales, seals, walrus or other living resources of the sea.

(6) *New ship* means a ship the keel of which is laid, or which is at a similar stage of construction, on or after the date of coming into force of the present Convention for each Contracting Government.

(7) *Existing ship* means a ship which is not a new ship.

P88 **(8)** *Length* means 96% of the total length on a waterline at 85% of the least moulded depth measured from the top of the keel, or the length from the fore side of the stem to the axis of the rudder stock on that waterline, if that be greater. Where the stem contour is concave above the waterline at 85% of the least moulded depth, both the forward terminal of the total length and the fore side of the stem respectively shall be taken at the vertical projection to that waterline of the aftermost point of the stem contour (above that waterline). In ships designed with a rake of keel the waterline on which this length is measured shall be parallel to the designed waterline.

---

see also the unified interpretation

P88 **(9)** *Anniversary date* means the day and the month of each year which will correspond to the date of expiry of the relevant certificate.

Article 3
General provisions

P88 **(1)**   No ship to which the present Convention applies shall proceed to sea on an international voyage after the date on which the present Convention comes into force unless it has been surveyed, marked and provided with an International Load Line Certificate or, where appropriate, an International Load Line Exemption Certificate in accordance with the provisions of the present Convention.

(2)   Nothing in this Convention shall prevent an Administration from assigning a greater freeboard than the minimum freeboard determined in accordance with annex I.

Article 4
Application

(1)   The present Convention shall apply to:

    (a) ships registered in countries the Governments of which are Contracting Governments;

(b) ships registered in territories to which the present Convention is extended under article 32; and

(c) unregistered ships flying the flag of a State, the Government of which is a Contracting Government.

(2) The present Convention shall apply to ships engaged on international voyages.

P88 **(3)** The regulations contained in annex I, unless expressly provided otherwise, are applicable to new ships.

(4) Existing ships which do not fully comply with the requirements of the regulations contained in annex I or any part thereof shall meet at least such lesser related requirements as the Administration applied to ships on international voyages prior to the coming into force of the present Convention; in no case shall such ships be required to increase their freeboards. In order to take advantage of any reduction in freeboard from that previously assigned, existing ships shall comply with all the requirements of the present Convention.

---
see also the unified interpretation
---

(5) The regulations contained in annex II are applicable to new and existing ships to which the present Convention applies.

Article 5
Exceptions

(1) The present Convention shall not apply to:

(a) ships of war;

(b) new ships of less than 24 metres in length;

(c) existing ships of less than 150 tons gross;

(d) pleasure yachts not engaged in trade;

(e) fishing vessels.

(2) Nothing herein shall apply to ships solely navigating:

(a) the Great Lakes of North America and the River St. Lawrence as far east as a rhumb line drawn from Cap des Rosiers to West Point, Anticosti Island, and, on the north side of Anticosti Island, the meridian of longitude 63° W;

(b) the Caspian Sea;

P88 **(c)** the Plate, Parana and Uruguay Rivers as far east as a rhumb line drawn between Punta Rasa (Cabo San Antonio), Argentina, and Punta del Este, Uruguay.

Article 6
Exemptions

(1) Ships when engaged on international voyages between the near neighbouring ports of two or more States may be exempted by the

Administration from the provisions of the present Convention, so long as they shall remain engaged on such voyages, if the Governments of the States in which such ports are situated shall be satisfied that the sheltered nature or conditions of such voyages between such ports make it unreasonable or impracticable to apply the provisions of the present Convention to ships engaged on such voyages.

(2) The Administration may exempt any ship which embodies features of a novel kind from any of the provisions of this Convention the application of which might seriously impede research into the development of such features and their incorporation in ships engaged on international voyages. Any such ship shall, however, comply with safety requirements which, in the opinion of that Administration, are adequate for the service for which it is intended and are such as to ensure the overall safety of the ship and which are acceptable to the Governments of the States to be visited by the ship.

(3) The Administration which allows any exemption under paragraphs (1) and (2) of this article shall communicate to the Inter-Governmental Maritime Consultative Organization* (hereinafter called "the Organization") particulars of the same and reasons therefor which the Organization shall circulate to the Contracting Governments for their information.

(4) A ship which is not normally engaged on international voyages but which, in exceptional circumstances, is required to undertake a single international voyage may be exempted by the Administration from any of the requirements of the present Convention, provided that it complies with safety requirements which, in the opinion of that Administration, are adequate for the voyage which is to be undertaken by the ship.

Article 7
Force majeure

(1) A ship which is not subject to the provisions of the present Convention at the time of its departure on any voyage shall not become subject to such provisions on account of any deviation from its intended voyage due to stress of weather or any other cause of *force majeure*.

(2) In applying the provisions of the present Convention, the Contracting Government shall give due consideration to any deviation or delay caused to any ship owing to stress of weather or any other cause of *force majeure*.

Article 8
Equivalents

(1) The Administration may allow any fitting, material, appliance or apparatus to be fitted, or any other provision to be made in a ship, other than that required by the present Convention, if it is satisfied by trial thereof or otherwise that such fitting, material, appliance or apparatus, or provision, is at least as effective as that required by the Convention.

---

* The name of the Organization was changed to "International Maritime Organization" by virtue of amendments to the Organization's Convention which entered into force on 22 May 1982.

(2) The Administration which allows a fitting, material, appliance or apparatus, or provision, other than that required by the present Convention, shall communicate to the Organization for circulation to the Contracting Governments particulars thereof, together with a report on any trials made.

Article 9
Approvals for experimental purposes

(1) Nothing in the present Convention shall prevent an Administration from making specific approvals for experimental purposes in respect of a ship to which the Convention applies.

(2) An Administration which makes any such approval shall communicate to the Organization for circulation to the Contracting Governments particulars thereof.

Article 10
Repairs, alterations and modifications

(1) A ship which undergoes repairs, alterations, modifications and outfitting related thereto shall continue to comply with at least the requirements previously applicable to the ship. An existing ship in such a case shall not, as a rule, comply to a lesser extent with the requirements for a new ship than it did before.

(2) Repairs, alterations and modifications of a major character and outfitting related thereto should meet the requirements for a new ship in so far as the Administration deems reasonable and practicable.

Article 11
Zones and areas

(1) A ship to which the present Convention applies shall comply with the requirements applicable to that ship in the zones and areas described in annex II.

(2) A port standing on the boundary line between two zones or areas shall be regarded as within the zone or area from or into which the ship arrives or departs.

Article 12
Submersion

(1) Except as provided in paragraphs (2) and (3) of this article, the appropriate load lines on the sides of the ship corresponding to the season of the year and the zone or area in which the ship may be shall not be submerged at any time when the ship puts to sea, during the voyage or on arrival.

P88 **(2)** When a ship is in fresh water of unit density the appropriate load line may be submerged by the amount of the fresh water allowance shown on the International Load Line Certificate. Where the density is other than unity, an allowance shall be made proportional to the difference between 1.025 and the actual density.

(3) When a ship departs from a port situated on a river or inland waters, deeper loading shall be permitted corresponding to the weight of fuel and all other materials required for consumption between the point of departure and the sea.

Article 13
P88 *Surveys and marking*

P88 The surveys and marking of ships, as regards the enforcement of the provisions of the present Convention and the granting of exemptions therefrom, shall be carried out by officers of the Administration. The Administration may, however, entrust the surveys and marking either to surveyors nominated for the purpose or to organizations recognized by it. In every case the Administration concerned fully guarantees the completeness and efficiency of the survey and marking.

Article 14
P88 *Initial, renewal and annual surveys*

P88 **(1)** A ship shall be subjected to the surveys specified below:

(a) An initial survey before the ship is put in service, which shall include a complete inspection of its structure and equipment in so far as the ship is covered by the present Convention. The survey shall be such as to ensure that the arrangements, materials and scantlings fully comply with the requirements of the present Convention.

(b) A renewal survey at intervals specified by the Administration but not exceeding five years, except where paragraphs (2), (5), (6) and (7) of article 19 are applicable, which shall be such as to ensure that the structure, equipment, arrangements, materials and scantlings fully comply with the requirements of the present Convention.

(c) An annual survey within 3 months before or after each anniversary date of the certificate to ensure that:

(i) alterations have not been made to the hull or superstructures which would affect the calculations determining the position of the load line;

(ii) the fittings and appliances for the protection of openings, guard rails, freeing ports and means of access to crew's quarters are maintained in an effective condition;

(iii) the freeboard marks are correctly and permanently indicated;

(iv) the information required by regulation 10 is provided.

P88 **(2)** The annual surveys referred to in paragraph (1)(c) of this article shall be endorsed on the International Load Line Certificate or the International Load Line Exemption Certificate issued to a ship exempted under paragraph (2) of article 6 of the present Convention.

Article 15
Maintenance of conditions after survey

After any survey of the ship under article 14 has been completed, no change shall be made in the structure, equipment, arrangements, material or scantlings covered by the survey, without the sanction of the Administration.

Article 16
Issue of certificates

[P88] **(1)**   An International Load Line Certificate shall be issued to every ship which has been surveyed and marked in accordance with the present Convention.

(2)   An International Load Line Exemption Certificate shall be issued to any ship to which an exemption has been granted under and in accordance with paragraph (2) or (4) of article 6.

(3)   Such certificates shall be issued by the Administration or by any person or organization duly authorized by it. In every case, the Administration assumes full responsibility for the certificate.

[P88] **(4)**

Article 17
[P88] *Issue or endorsement of certificates*
by another Government

[P88] **(1)**   A Contracting Government may, at the request of another Contracting Government, cause a ship to be surveyed and, if satisfied that the provisions of the present Convention are complied with, shall issue or authorize the issue of an International Load Line Certificate to the ship and, where appropriate, endorse or authorize the endorsement of the certificate on the ship in accordance with the present Convention.

(2)   A copy of the certificate, a copy of the survey report used for computing the freeboard, and a copy of the computations shall be transmitted as early as possible to the requesting Government.

(3)   A certificate so issued must contain a statement to the effect that it has been issued at the request of the Government of the State whose flag the ship is or will be flying and it shall have the same force and receive the same recognition as a certificate issued under article 16.

[P88] **(4)**   No International Load Line Certificate shall be issued to a ship which is flying the flag of a State the Government of which is not a Contracting Government.

Article 18
Form of certificates

[P88] The certificates shall be drawn up in the form corresponding to the models given in annex III to the present Convention. If the language used is neither

English nor French, the text shall include a translation into one of these languages.

<hr>

see also the unified interpretation

<hr>

Article 19
P88 *Duration and validity of certificates*

P88 **(1)** An International Load Line Certificate shall be issued for a period specified by the Administration, which shall not exceed 5 years.

P88 **(2)** **(a)** Notwithstanding the requirements of paragraph (1), when the renewal survey is completed within 3 months before the expiry date of the existing certificate, the new certificate shall be valid from the date of completion of the renewal survey to a date not exceeding 5 years from the date of expiry of the existing certificate.

(b) When the renewal survey is completed after the expiry date of the existing certificate, the new certificate shall be valid from the date of completion of the renewal survey to a date not exceeding 5 years from the date of expiry of the existing certificate.

(c) When the renewal survey is completed more than 3 months before the expiry date of the existing certificate, the new certificate shall be valid from the date of completion of the renewal survey to a date not exceeding 5 years from the date of completion of the renewal survey.

P88 **(3)** If a certificate is issued for a period of less than 5 years, the Administration may extend the validity of a certificate beyond the expiry date to the maximum period specified in paragraph (1), provided that the annual surveys referred to in article 14 applicable when a certificate is issued for a period of 5 years are carried out as appropriate.

P88 **(4)** If, after the renewal survey referred to in paragraph (1)(b) of article 14, a new certificate cannot be issued to the ship before the expiry date of the existing certificate, the person or organization carrying out the survey may extend the validity of the existing certificate for a period which shall not exceed 5 months. This extension shall be endorsed on the certificate, and shall be granted only where there have been no alterations in the structure, equipment, arrangements, materials or scantlings which affect the ship's freeboard.

P88 **(5)** If a ship at the time when a certificate expires is not in a port in which it is to be surveyed, the Administration may extend the period of validity of the certificate but this extension shall be granted only for the purpose of allowing the ship to complete its voyage to the port in which it is to be surveyed, and then only in cases where it appears proper and reasonable to do so. No certificate shall be extended for a period longer than 3 months, and a ship to which an extension is granted shall not, on its arrival in the port in which it is to be surveyed, be entitled by virtue of such extension to leave that port without having a new certificate. When the renewal survey is completed, the new certificate shall be valid to a date not exceeding 5 years from the date of expiry of the existing certificate before the extension was granted.

P88 **(6)** A certificate issued to a ship engaged on short voyages which has not been extended under the foregoing provisions of this article may be extended by the Administration for a period of grace of up to one month from the date of expiry stated on it. When the renewal survey is completed the new certificate shall be valid to a date not exceeding 5 years from the date of expiry of the existing certificate before the extension was granted.

P88 **(7)**   In special circumstances, as determined by the Administration, a new certificate need not be dated from the expiry of the existing certificate as required by paragraphs (2), (5) and (6). In these special circumstances, the new certificate shall be valid to a date not exceeding 5 years from the date of completion of the renewal survey.

P88 **(8)**   If an annual survey is completed before the period specified in article 14 then:

(a)   the anniversary date shown on the certificate shall be amended by endorsement to a date which shall not be more than 3 months later than the date on which the survey was completed;

(b)   the subsequent annual survey required by article 14 shall be completed at the intervals prescribed by that article using the new anniversary date;

(c)   the expiry date may remain unchanged provided one or more annual surveys are carried out so that the maximum intervals between the surveys prescribed by article 14 are not exceeded.

P88 **(9)**   An International Load Line Certificate shall cease to be valid if any of the following circumstances exist:

(a)   material alterations have taken place in the hull or superstructures of the ship such as would necessitate the assignment of an increased freeboard;

(b)   the fittings and appliances mentioned in paragraph (1)(c) of article 14 are not maintained in an effective condition;

(c)   the certificate is not endorsed to show that the ship has been surveyed as provided in paragraph (1)(c) of article 14;

(d)   the structural strength of the ship is lowered to such an extent that the ship is unsafe.

P88 **(10)**   **(a)**   The duration of an International Load Line Exemption Certificate issued by an Administration to a ship exempted under paragraph (2) of article 6 shall not exceed 5 years. Such certificate shall be subject to a renewal, endorsement, extension and cancellation procedure similar to that provided for an International Load Line Certificate under this article.

(b)   The duration of an International Load Line Exemption Certificate issued to a ship exempted under paragraph (4) of article 6 shall be limited to the single voyage for which it is issued.

P88 **(11)**   A certificate issued to a ship by an Administration shall cease to be valid upon the transfer of such a ship to the flag of another State.

Article 20
Acceptance of certificates

The certificates issued under the authority of a Contracting Government in accordance with the present Convention shall be accepted by the other Contracting Governments and regarded for all purposes covered by the present Convention as having the same force as certificates issued by them.

Article 21
Control

P88 **(1)** Ships holding a certificate issued under article 16 or article 17 are subject, when in the ports of other Contracting Governments, to control by officers duly authorized by such Governments. Contracting Governments shall ensure that such control is exercised as far as is reasonable and practicable with a view to verifying that there is on board a valid certificate under the present Convention. If there is a valid International Load Line Certificate on board the ship, such control shall be limited to the purpose of determining that:

(a) the ship is not loaded beyond the limits allowed by the certificate;

(b) the position of the load line of the ship corresponds with the certificate; and

P88 **(c)** the ship has not been so materially altered in respect of the matters set out in sub-paragraphs (a) and (b) of paragraph (9) of article 19 that the ship is manifestly unfit to proceed to sea without danger to human life.

If there is a valid International Load Line Exemption Certificate on board, such control shall be limited to the purpose of determining that any conditions stipulated in that certificate are complied with.

(2) If such control is exercised under sub-paragraph (c) of paragraph (1) of this article, it shall only be exercised in so far as may be necessary to ensure that the ship shall not sail until it can proceed to sea without danger to the passengers or the crew.

(3) In the event of the control provided for in this article giving rise to intervention of any kind, the officer carrying out the control shall immediately inform in writing the Consul or the diplomatic representative of the State whose flag the ship is flying of this decision and of all the circumstances in which intervention was deemed to be necessary.

Article 22
Privileges

The privileges of the present Convention may not be claimed in favour of any ship unless it holds a valid certificate under the Convention.

Article 23
Casualties

(1) Each Administration undertakes to conduct an investigation of any casualty occurring to ships for which it is responsible and which are subject to the provisions of the present Convention when it judges that such an investigation may assist in determining what changes in the Convention might be desirable.

(2) Each Contracting Government undertakes to supply the Organization with the pertinent information concerning the findings of such investigations. No reports or recommendations of the Organization based upon such information shall disclose the identity or nationality of the ships concerned or in any manner fix or imply responsibility upon any ship or person.

Article 24
Prior treaties and conventions

(1) All other treaties, conventions and arrangements relating to load line matters at present in force between Governments Parties to the present Convention shall continue to have full and complete effect during the terms thereof as regards:

    (a) ships to which the present Convention does not apply; and

    (b) ships to which the present Convention applies, in respect of matters for which it has not expressly provided.

(2) To the extent, however, that such treaties, conventions or arrangements conflict with the provisions of the present Convention, the provisions of the present Convention shall prevail.

Article 25
Special rules drawn up by agreement

When in accordance with the present Convention special rules are drawn up by agreement among all or some of the Contracting Governments, such rules shall be communicated to the Organization for circulation to all Contracting Governments.

Article 26
Communication of information

(1) The Contracting Governments undertake to communicate to and deposit with the Organization:

    (a) a sufficient number of specimens of their certificates issued under the provisions of the present Convention for circulation to the Contracting Governments;

    (b) the text of the laws, decrees, orders, regulations and other instruments which shall have been promulgated on the various matters within the scope of the present Convention; and

(c) a list of non-governmental agencies which are authorized to act in their behalf in the administration of load line matters for circulation to the Contracting Governments.

(2) Each Contracting Government agrees to make its strength standards available to any other Contracting Government, upon request.

Article 27
Signature, acceptance and accession

(1) The present Convention shall remain open for signature for three months from 5 April 1966 and shall thereafter remain open for accession. Governments of States Members of the United Nations, or of any of the Specialized Agencies, or of the International Atomic Energy Agency, or parties to the Statute of the International Court of Justice may become parties to the Convention by:

(a) signature without reservation as to acceptance;

(b) signature subject to acceptance followed by acceptance; or

(c) accession.

(2) Acceptance or accession shall be effected by the deposit of an instrument of acceptance or accession with the Organization which shall inform all Governments that have signed the Convention or acceded to it of each new acceptance or accession and of the date of its deposit.

Article 28
Coming into force

(1) The present Convention shall come into force twelve months after the date on which not less than fifteen Governments of the States, including seven each with not less than one million gross tons of shipping, have signed without reservation as to acceptance or deposited instruments of acceptance or accession in accordance with article 27. The Organization shall inform all Governments which have signed or acceded to the present Convention of the date on which it comes into force.

(2) For Governments which have deposited an instrument of acceptance of or accession to the present Convention during the twelve months mentioned in paragraph (1) of this article, the acceptance or accession shall take effect on the coming into force of the present Convention or three months after the date of deposit of the instrument of acceptance or accession, whichever is the later date.

(3) For Governments which have deposited an instrument of acceptance of or accession to the present Convention after the date on which it comes into force, the Convention shall come into force three months after the date of the deposit of such instrument.

(4) After the date on which all the measures required to bring an amendment to the present Convention into force have been completed, or all necessary acceptances are deemed to have been given under sub-paragraph (b) of paragraph (2) of article 29 in case of amendment by unanimous acceptance, any instrument of acceptance or accession deposited shall be deemed to apply to the Convention as amended.

Article 29
Amendments

(1)   The present Convention may be amended upon the proposal of a Contracting Government by any of the procedures specified in this article.

(2)   Amendment by unanimous acceptance:

(a)   Upon the request of a Contracting Government, any amendment proposed by it to the present Convention shall be communicated by the Organization to all Contracting Governments for consideration with a view to unanimous acceptance.

(b)   Any such amendment shall enter into force twelve months after the date of its acceptance by all Contracting Governments unless an earlier date is agreed upon. A Contracting Government which does not communicate its acceptance or rejection of the amendment to the Organization within three years of its first communication by the latter shall be deemed to have accepted the amendment.

(c)   Any proposed amendment shall be deemed to be rejected if it is not accepted under sub-paragraph (b) of the present paragraph within three years after it has been first communicated to all Contracting Governments by the Organization.

(3)   Amendment after consideration in the Organization:

(a)   Upon the request of a Contracting Government, any amendment proposed by it to the present Convention will be considered in the Organization. If adopted by a majority of two-thirds of those present and voting in the Maritime Safety Committee of the Organization, such amendment shall be communicated to all Members of the Organization and all Contracting Governments at least six months prior to its consideration by the Assembly of the Organization.

(b)   If adopted by a two-thirds majority of those present and voting in the Assembly, the amendment shall be communicated by the Organization to all Contracting Governments for their acceptance.

(c)   Such amendment shall come into force twelve months after the date on which it is accepted by two-thirds of the Contracting Governments. The amendment shall come into force with respect to all Contracting Governments except those which, before it comes into force, make a declaration that they do not accept the amendment.

(d)   The Assembly, by a two-thirds majority of those present and voting, including two-thirds of the Governments represented on the Maritime Safety Committee and present and voting in the

Assembly, may propose a determination at the time of its adoption that an amendment is of such an important nature that any Contracting Government which makes a declaration under sub-paragraph (c), and which does not accept the amendment within a period of twelve months after it comes into force, shall cease to be a party to the present Convention upon the expiry of that period. This determination shall be subject to the prior acceptance of two-thirds of the Contracting Governments to the present Convention.

(e) Nothing in this paragraph shall prevent the Contracting Government which first proposed action under this paragraph on an amendment to the present Convention from taking at any time such alternative action as it deems desirable in accordance with paragraph (2) or (4) of this article.

(4) Amendment by a conference:

(a) Upon the request of a Contracting Government, concurred in by at least one-third of the Contracting Governments, a conference of Governments will be convened by the Organization to consider amendments to the present Convention.

(b) Every amendment adopted by such a conference by a two-thirds majority of those present and voting of the Contracting Governments shall be communicated by the Organization to all Contracting Governments for their acceptance.

(c) Such amendment shall come into force twelve months after the date on which it is accepted by two-thirds of the Contracting Governments. The amendment shall come into force with respect to all Contracting Governments except those which, before it comes into force, make a declaration that they do not accept the amendment.

(d) By a two-thirds majority of those present and voting, a conference convened under sub-paragraph (a) may determine at the time of its adoption that an amendment is of such an important nature that any Contracting Government which makes a declaration under sub-paragraph (c), and which does not accept the amendment within a period of twelve months after it comes into force, shall cease to be a party to the present Convention upon the expiry of that period.

(5) Any amendments to the present Convention made under this article which relate to the structure of a ship shall apply only to ships the keels of which are laid, or which are at a similar stage of construction, on or after the date on which the amendment comes into force.

(6) The Organization shall inform all Contracting Governments of any amendments which come into force under this article, together with the date on which each such amendment will come into force.

(7) Any acceptance or declaration under this article shall be made by a notification in writing to the Organization which shall notify all Contracting Governments of the receipt of the acceptance or declaration.

Article 30
Denunciation

(1) The present Convention may be denounced by any Contracting Government at any time after the expiry of five years from the date on which the Convention comes into force for that Government.

(2) Denunciation shall be effected by a notification in writing addressed to the Organization which shall inform all the other Contracting Governments of any such notification received and of the date of its receipt.

(3) A denunciation shall take effect one year, or such longer period as may be specified in the notification, after its receipt by the Organization.

Article 31
Suspension

(1) In case of hostilities or other extraordinary circumstances which affect the vital interests of a State the Government of which is a Contracting Government, that Government may suspend the operation of the whole or any part of the present Convention. The suspending Government shall immediately give notice of any such suspension to the Organization.

(2) Such suspension shall not deprive other Contracting Governments of any right of control under the present Convention over the ships of the suspending Government when such ships are within their ports.

(3) The suspending Government may at any time terminate such suspension and shall immediately give notice of such termination to the Organization.

(4) The Organization shall notify all Contracting Governments of any suspension or termination of suspension under this article.

Article 32
Territories

(1) **(a)** The United Nations, in cases where they are the administering authority for a territory, or any Contracting Government responsible for the international relations of a territory, shall as soon as possible consult with such territory in an endeavour to extend the present Convention to that territory and may at any time by notification in writing to the Organization declare that the present Convention shall extend to such territory.

(b) The present Convention shall, from the date of the receipt of the notification or from such other date as may be specified in the notification, extend to the territory named therein.

(2) **(a)** The United Nations, or any Contracting Government which has made a declaration under sub-paragraph (a) of paragraph (1) of this article, at any time after the expiry of a period of five years from the date on which the Convention has been so extended to any territory, may by notification in writing to the Organization declare that the present Convention shall cease to extend to any such territory named in the notification.

(b) The present Convention shall cease to extend to any territory mentioned in such notification one year, or such longer period as may be specified therein, after the date of receipt of the notification by the Organization.

(3) The Organization shall inform all the Contracting Governments of the extension of the present Convention to any territories under paragraph (1) of this article, and of the termination of any such extension under the provisions of paragraph (2), stating in each case the date from which the present Convention has been or will cease to be so extended.

Article 33
Registration

(1) The present Convention shall be deposited with the Organization and the Secretary-General of the Organization shall transmit certified true copies thereof to all Signatory Governments and to all Governments which accede to the present Convention.

(2) As soon as the present Convention comes into force it shall be registered by the Organization in accordance with Article 102 of the Charter of the United Nations.

Article 34
Languages

The present Convention is established in a single copy in the English and French languages, both texts being equally authentic. Official translations in the Russian and Spanish languages shall be prepared and deposited with the signed original.

IN WITNESS WHEREOF the undersigned being duly authorized by their respective Governments for that purpose have signed the present Convention.*

DONE at London this fifth day of April 1966.

---

* Signatures omitted.

Annex B
Annexes to the Convention as modified by the Protocol of 1988 relating thereto

Annex I
Regulations for determining load lines

Chapter I
General

The regulations assume that the nature and stowage of the cargo, ballast, etc., are such as to secure sufficient stability of the ship and the avoidance of excessive structural stress.

The regulations also assume that where there are international requirements relating to stability or subdivision, these requirements have been complied with.

Regulation 1
P88 *Strength and intact stability of ships*

P88 **(1)**   The Administration shall satisfy itself that the general structural strength of the ship is adequate for the draught corresponding to the freeboard assigned.

P88 **(2)**   A ship which is designed, constructed and maintained in compliance with the appropriate requirements of an organization, including a classification society, which is recognized by the Administration or with applicable national standards of the Administration in accordance with the provisions of regulation 2-1, may be considered to provide an acceptable level of strength. The above provisions shall apply to all structures, equipment and fittings covered by this annex for which standards for strength and construction are not expressly provided.

P88 **(3)**   Ships shall comply with an intact stability standard acceptable to the Administration.

Regulation 2
Application

P88 **(1)**   Ships with mechanical means of propulsion or lighters, barges or other ships without independent means of propulsion, shall be assigned freeboards in accordance with the provisions of regulations 1 to 40, inclusive.

[P88] **(2)** Ships carrying timber deck cargoes may be assigned, in addition to the freeboards prescribed in paragraph (1), timber freeboards in accordance with the provisions of regulations 41 to 45.

[P88] **(3)** Ships designed to carry sail, whether as the sole means of propulsion or as a supplementary means, and tugs, shall be assigned freeboards in accordance with the provisions of regulations 1 to 40, inclusive. Additional freeboard may be required as determined by the Administration.

(4) Ships of wood or of composite construction, or of other materials the use of which the Administration has approved, or ships whose constructional features are such as to render the application of the provisions of this annex unreasonable or impracticable, shall be assigned freeboards as determined by the Administration.

[P88] **(5)** Regulations 10 to 26, inclusive, shall apply to every ship to which a minimum freeboard is assigned. Relaxations from these requirements may be granted to a ship to which a greater than minimum freeboard is assigned, on condition that the Administration is satisfied with the safety conditions provided.

[P88] **(6)** Where the assigned summer freeboard is increased such that the resulting draught is not more than that corresponding to a minimum summer freeboard for the same ship, but with an assumed freeboard deck located a distance below the actual freeboard deck at least equal to the standard superstructure height, the conditions of assignment in accordance with regulations 12, 14-1 through 20, 23, 24 and 25, as applicable, to the actual freeboard deck may be as required for a superstructure deck.

[P88] **(7)** Unless expressly provided otherwise, the regulations of this annex shall apply to ships the keels of which are laid or which are at a similar stage of construction on or after 1 January 2005.

[P88] **(8)** For ships the keels of which are laid or which are at a similar stage of construction before 1 January 2005, the Administration shall ensure that the requirements which are applicable under the International Convention on Load Lines, 1966, as modified by the Protocol of 1988 relating thereto, adopted by the International Conference on Harmonized System of Survey and Certification, 1988, are complied with.

[P88] **(9)** High-speed craft which comply with the requirements of the International Code of Safety for High-Speed Craft, 2000 (2000 HSC Code), adopted by the Maritime Safety Committee of the Organization by resolution MSC.97(73), and which have been surveyed and certified as provided in the Code shall be deemed to have complied with the requirements of this annex. The certificates and permits issued under the 2000 HSC Code shall have the same force and the same recognition as the certificates issued under this annex.

[P88] # Regulation 2-1
[P88] *Authorization of recognized organizations*

[P88] Organizations, including classification societies, referred to in article 13 of the Convention and regulation 1(2) shall comply with the guidelines adopted by the Organization by resolution A.739(18), as may be amended by the

Organization, and the specifications adopted by the Organization by resolution A.789(19), as may be amended by the Organization, provided that such amendments are adopted, brought into force and take effect in accordance with the provisions of article VI of the present Protocol.

Regulation 3
Definitions of terms used in the annexes

P88 **(1)**   *Length*

P88 **(a)**   The length (*L*) shall be taken as 96% of the total length on a waterline at 85% of the least moulded depth measured from the top of the keel, or as the length from the fore side of the stem to the axis of the rudder stock on that waterline, if that be greater.

P88 **(b)**   For ships without a rudder stock, the length (*L*) is to be taken as 96% of the waterline at 85% of the least moulded depth.

P88 **(c)**   Where the stem contour is concave above the waterline at 85% of the least moulded depth, both the forward terminal of the total length and the fore side of the stem respectively shall be taken at the vertical projection to that waterline of the aftermost point of the stem contour (above that waterline) (see figure 3.1).

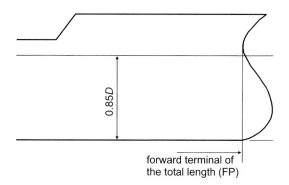

0.85*D*

forward terminal of
the total length (FP)

Figure 3.1

P88 **(d)**   In ships designed with a rake of keel, the waterline on which this length is measured shall be parallel to the designed waterline at 85% of the least moulded depth D_{min}, found by drawing a line parallel to the keel line of the vessel (including skeg) tangent to the moulded sheer line of the freeboard deck. The least moulded depth is the vertical distance measured from the top of the keel to the top of the freeboard deck beam at side at the point of tangency (see figure 3.2).

(2)   *Perpendiculars.* The forward and after perpendiculars shall be taken at the forward and after ends of the length (*L*). The forward perpendicular shall coincide with the fore side of the stem on the waterline on which the length is measured.

111

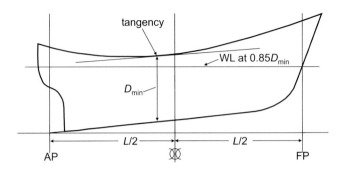

Figure 3.2

(3) *Amidships.* Amidships is at the middle of the length (L).

(4) *Breadth.* Unless expressly provided otherwise, the breadth (B) is the maximum breadth of the ship, measured amidships to the moulded line of the frame in a ship with a metal shell and to the outer surface of the hull in a ship with a shell of any other material.

(5) *Moulded depth*

    (a) The moulded depth is the vertical distance measured from the top of the keel to the top of the freeboard deck beam at side. In wood and composite ships the distance is measured from the lower edge of the keel rabbet. Where the form at the lower part of the midship section is of a hollow character, or where thick garboards are fitted, the distance is measured from the point where the line of the flat of the bottom continued inwards cuts the side of the keel.

    P88 **(b)** In ships having rounded gunwales, the moulded depth shall be measured to the point of intersection of the moulded lines of deck and sides, the lines extending as though the gunwale were of angular design.

    (c) Where the freeboard deck is stepped and the raised part of the deck extends over the point at which the moulded depth is to be determined, the moulded depth shall be measured to a line of reference extending from the lower part of the deck along a line parallel with the raised part.

---

see also the unified interpretation

---

(6) *Depth for freeboard (D)*

    P88 **(a)** The depth for freeboard (D) is the moulded depth amidships, plus the freeboard deck thickness at side.

    (b) The depth for freeboard (D) in a ship having a rounded gunwale with a radius greater than 4% of the breadth (B) or having topsides of unusual form is the depth for freeboard of a ship having a midship section with vertical topsides and with the same round of beam and area of topside section equal to that provided by the actual midship section.

P88 **(7)** *Block coefficient*

P88 **(a)** The block coefficient (C_b) is given by:

$$C_b = \frac{\nabla}{L \cdot B \cdot d_1}; \text{ where}$$

∇ is the volume of the moulded displacement of the ship, excluding appendages, in a ship with a metal shell, and is the volume of displacement to the outer surface of the hull in a ship with a shell of any other material, both taken at a moulded draught of d_1; and where

d_1 is 85% of the least moulded depth.

P88 **(b)** When calculating the block coefficient of a multi-hull craft, the full breadth (B) as defined in paragraph (4) is to be used and not the breadth of a single hull.

(8) *Freeboard.* The freeboard assigned is the distance measured vertically downwards amidships from the upper edge of the deck line to the upper edge of the related load line.

P88 **(9)** *Freeboard deck*

P88 **(a)** The freeboard deck is normally the uppermost complete deck exposed to weather and sea, which has permanent means of closing all openings in the weather part thereof, and below which all openings in the sides of the ship are fitted with permanent means of watertight closing.

P88 **(b)** Lower deck as a freeboard deck

At the option of the owner and subject to the approval of the Administration, a lower deck may be designated as the freeboard deck provided it is a complete and permanent deck continuous in a fore and aft direction at least between the machinery space and peak bulkheads and continuous athwartships.

(i) When this lower deck is stepped, the lowest line of the deck and the continuation of that line parallel to the upper part of the deck is taken as the freeboard deck.

(ii) When a lower deck is designated as the freeboard deck, that part of the hull which extends above the freeboard deck is treated as a superstructure so far as concerns the application of the conditions of assignment and the calculation of freeboard. It is from this deck that the freeboard is calculated.

(iii) When a lower deck is designated as the freeboard deck, such deck as a minimum shall consist of suitably framed stringers at the ship sides and transversely at each watertight bulkhead which extends to the upper deck, within cargo spaces. The width of these stringers shall not be less than can be conveniently fitted having regard to the structure and the operation of the ship. Any arrangement of stringers shall be such that structural requirements can also be met.

[P88] **(c)** Discontinuous freeboard deck, stepped freeboard deck

(i) Where a recess in the freeboard deck extends to the sides of the ship and is in excess of one metre in length, the lowest line of the exposed deck and the continuation of that line parallel to the upper part of the deck is taken as the freeboard deck (see figure 3.3).

(ii) Where a recess in the freeboard deck does not extend to the sides of the ship, the upper part of the deck is taken as the freeboard deck.

(iii) Recesses not extending from side to side in a deck below the exposed deck, designated as the freeboard deck, may be disregarded, provided all openings in the weather deck are fitted with weathertight closing appliances.

(iv) Due regard shall be given to the drainage of exposed recesses and to free surface effects on stability.

(v) The provisions of subparagraphs (i) through (iv) are not intended to apply to dredgers, hopper barges or other similar types of ships with large open holds, where each case requires individual consideration.

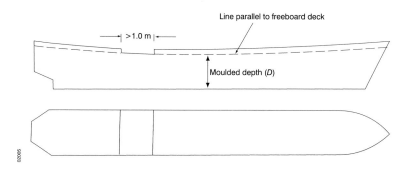

Figure 3.3

(10) *Superstructure*

[P88] **(a)** A superstructure is a decked structure on the freeboard deck, extending from side to side of the ship or with the side plating not being inboard of the shell plating more than 4% of the breadth (*B*).

(b) An enclosed superstructure is a superstructure with:

(i) enclosing bulkheads of efficient construction;

(ii) access openings, if any, in these bulkheads fitted with doors complying with the requirements of regulation 12;

(iii) all other openings in sides or ends of the superstructure fitted with efficient weathertight means of closing.

[P88] A bridge or poop shall not be regarded as enclosed unless access is provided for the crew starting from any point on the uppermost complete exposed deck or higher to reach machinery and other working spaces inside these superstructures by alternative means which are available at all times when bulkhead openings are closed.

(c) The height of a superstructure is the least vertical height measured at side from the top of the superstructure deck beams to the top of the freeboard deck beams.

(d) The length of a superstructure (*S*) is the mean length of the part of the superstructure which lies within the length (*L*).

P88 **(e)** *Bridge.* A bridge is a superstructure which does not extend to either the forward or after perpendicular.

P88 **(f)** *Poop.* A poop is a superstructure which extends from the after perpendicular forward to a point which is aft of the forward perpendicular. The poop may originate from a point aft of the after perpendicular.

P88 **(g)** *Forecastle.* A forecastle is a superstructure which extends from the forward perpendicular aft to a point which is forward of the after perpendicular. The forecastle may originate from a point forward of the forward perpendicular.

P88 **(h)** *Full superstructure.* A full superstructure is a superstructure which, as a minimum, extends from the forward to the after perpendicular.

P88 **(i)** *Raised quarterdeck.* A raised quarterdeck is a superstructure which extends forward from the after perpendicular, generally has a height less than a normal superstructure, and has an intact front bulkhead (sidescuttles of the non-opening type fitted with efficient deadlights and bolted manhole covers) (see figure 3.4). Where the forward bulkhead is not intact due to doors and access openings, the superstructure is then to be considered as a poop.

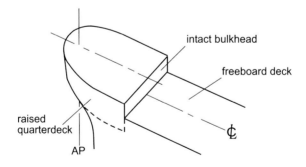

Figure 3.4

P88 **(11)** *Superstructure deck.* A superstructure deck is a deck forming the upper boundary of a superstructure.

P88 **(12)** *Flush deck ship.* A flush deck ship is one which has no superstructure on the freeboard deck.

P88 **(13)** *Weathertight.* "Weathertight" means that in any sea conditions water will not penetrate into the ship.

P88 **(14)** *Watertight.* "Watertight" means capable of preventing the passage of water through the structure in either direction with a proper margin of resistance under the pressure due to the maximum head of water which it might have to sustain.

P88 **(15)** *Well.* A well is any area on the deck exposed to the weather, where water may be entrapped. Wells are considered to be deck areas bounded on two or more sides by deck structures.

Regulation 4
Deck line

P88 The deck line is a horizontal line 300 mm in length and 25 mm in breadth. It shall be marked amidships on each side of the ship, and its upper edge shall normally pass through the point where the continuation outwards of the upper surface of the freeboard deck intersects the outer surface of the shell (as illustrated in figure 4.1), provided that the deck line may be placed with reference to another fixed point on the ship on condition that the freeboard is correspondingly corrected. The location of the reference point and the identification of the freeboard deck shall in all cases be indicated on the International Load Line Certificate.

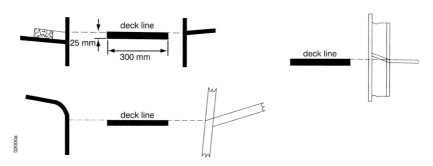

P88 **Figure 4.1** – *Deck line*

Regulation 5
P88 *Load line mark*

P88 The load line mark shall consist of a ring 300 mm in outside diameter and 25 mm wide which is intersected by a horizontal line 450 mm in length and 25 mm in breadth, the upper edge of which passes through the centre of the ring. The centre of the ring shall be placed amidships and at a distance equal to the assigned summer freeboard measured vertically below the upper edge of the deck line (as illustrated in figure 6.1).

Regulation 6

P88 *Lines to be used with the load line mark*

P88 **(1)** The lines which indicate the load line assigned in accordance with these regulations shall be horizontal lines 230 mm in length and 25 mm in breadth which extend forward of, unless expressly provided otherwise, and at right angles to, a vertical line 25 mm in breadth marked at a distance 540 mm forward of the centre of the ring (as illustrated in figure 6.1).

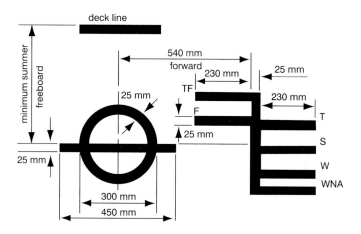

P88 **Figure 6.1** – *Load line mark and lines to be used with this mark*

(2) The following load lines shall be used:

(a) The Summer Load Line indicated by the upper edge of the line which passes through the centre of the ring and also by a line marked **S**.

(b) The Winter Load Line indicated by the upper edge of a line marked **W**.

(c) The Winter North Atlantic Load Line indicated by the upper edge of a line marked **WNA**.

(d) The Tropical Load Line indicated by the upper edge of a line marked **T**.

(e) The Fresh Water Load Line in summer indicated by the upper edge of a line marked **F**. The Fresh Water Load Line in summer is marked abaft the vertical line. The difference between the Fresh Water Load Line in summer and the Summer Load Line is the allowance to be made for loading in fresh water at the other load lines.

P88 **(f)** The Tropical Fresh Water Load Line indicated by the upper edge of a line marked **TF** and marked abaft the vertical line.

P88 **(3)** If timber freeboards are assigned in accordance with these regulations, the timber load lines shall be marked in addition to ordinary load lines. These lines shall be horizontal lines 230 mm in length and 25 mm in breadth which

117

extend abaft, unless expressly provided otherwise, and are at right angles to a vertical line 25 mm in breadth marked at a distance 540 mm abaft the centre of the ring (as illustrated in figure 6.2).

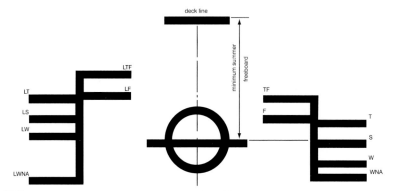

P88 **Figure 6.2** – *Timber load line mark and lines to be used with this mark*

(4)   The following timber load lines shall be used:

(a)   The Summer Timber Load Line indicated by the upper edge of a line marked **LS**.

(b)   The Winter Timber Load Line indicated by the upper edge of a line marked **LW**.

(c)   The Winter North Atlantic Timber Load Line indicated by the upper edge of a line marked **LWNA**.

(d)   The Tropical Timber Load Line indicated by the upper edge of a line marked **LT**.

(e)   The Fresh Water Timber Load Line in summer indicated by the upper edge of a line marked **LF** and marked forward of the vertical line. The difference between the Fresh Water Timber Load Line in summer and the Summer Timber Load Line is the allowance to be made for loading in fresh water at the other timber load lines.

(f)   The Tropical Fresh Water Timber Load Line indicated by the upper edge of a line marked **LTF** and marked forward of the vertical line.

(5)   Where the characteristics of a ship or the nature of the ship's service or navigational limits make any of the seasonal lines inapplicable, these lines may be omitted.

P88 **(6)**   Where a ship is assigned a greater than minimum freeboard so that the load line is marked at a position corresponding to, or lower than, the lowest seasonal load line assigned at minimum freeboard in accordance with the present Protocol, only the Fresh Water Load Line need be marked.

P88 **(7)**   Where a Winter North Atlantic Load Line is identical with the Winter Load Line corresponding to the same vertical line, this load line shall be marked **W**.

P88 **(8)**   Alternative/additional load lines required by other international conventions in force may be marked at right angles to and abaft the vertical line specified in paragraph (1).

Regulation 7
Mark of assigning Authority

The mark of the Authority by whom the load lines are assigned may be indicated alongside the load line ring above the horizontal line which passes through the centre of the ring, or above and below it. This mark shall consist of not more than four initials to identify the Authority's name, each measuring approximately 115 mm in height and 75 mm in width.

Regulation 8
Details of marking

The ring, lines and letters shall be painted in white or yellow on a dark ground or in black on a light ground. They shall also be permanently marked on the sides of the ships to the satisfaction of the Administration. The marks shall be plainly visible and, if necessary, special arrangements shall be made for this purpose.

see also the unified interpretation

Regulation 9
Verification of marks

P88 The International Load Line Certificate shall not be delivered to the ship until the officer or surveyor acting under the provisions of article 13 of the Convention has certified that the marks are correctly and permanently indicated on the ship's sides.

Chapter II
Conditions of assignment of freeboard

Regulation 10
Information to be supplied to the master

P88 **(1)** The master of every new ship shall be supplied with information to arrange for the loading and ballasting of his ship in such a way as to avoid the creation of any unacceptable stresses in the ship's structure, provided that this requirement need not apply to any particular length, design or class of ship where the Administration considers it to be unnecessary.

P88 **(2)** Information shall be provided to the master in a form that is approved by the Administration or a recognized organization. Stability information, and loading information also related to ship strength when required under paragraph (1), shall be carried on board at all times together with evidence that the information has been approved by the Administration.

P88 **(3)** A ship which is not required under the International Convention for Safety of Life at Sea in force to undergo an inclining test upon its completion shall:

  (a) be so inclined and the actual displacement and position of the centre of gravity shall be determined for the lightship condition;

  (b) if the Administration so approves, have its inclining test on completion dispensed with, provided basic stability data are available from the inclining test of a sister ship and it is shown to the satisfaction of the Administration that reliable stability information for the ship can be obtained from such basic data;

  (c) if the Administration decides that the performance of an inclining test is not practicable or safe or yields inaccurate results due to the specific proportions, arrangements, strength or hull form of a ship, have the ship's lightship characteristics determined by a detailed weight estimate confirmed by a lightweight survey;

  (d) have such information* supplied for the use of its master as is necessary to enable the master, by rapid and simple processes, to obtain accurate guidance as to the stability of the ship under all conditions likely to be encountered in normal service; and

  (e) carry on board at all times its approved stability information together with evidence that the information has been approved by the Administration.

P88 **(4)** Where any alterations are made to a ship so as to materially affect the loading or stability information supplied to the master, amended information shall be provided. If necessary the ship shall be re-inclined.

---

* Refer to the Code on Intact Stability for all Types of Ships covered by IMO Instruments, adopted by the Organization by resolution A.749(18), as amended.

Regulation 11
Superstructure end bulkheads

[P88] Bulkheads at exposed ends of enclosed superstructures shall be of an acceptable level of strength.

Regulation 12
Doors

see also the unified interpretation

(1)   All access openings in bulkheads at ends of enclosed superstructures shall be fitted with doors of steel or other equivalent material, permanently and strongly attached to the bulkhead, and framed, stiffened and fitted so that the whole structure is of equivalent strength to the un-pierced bulkhead and weathertight when closed. The means for securing these doors weathertight shall consist of gaskets and clamping devices or other equivalent means and shall be permanently attached to the bulkhead or to the doors themselves, and the doors shall be so arranged that they can be operated from both sides of the bulkhead.

[P88] **(2)**   Unless otherwise permitted by the Administration, doors shall open outwards to provide additional security against the impact of the sea.

[P88] **(3)**   Except as otherwise provided in these regulations, the height of the sills of access openings in bulkheads at ends of enclosed superstructures shall be at least 380 mm above the deck.

[P88] **(4)**   Portable sills shall be avoided. However, in order to facilitate the loading/unloading of heavy spare parts or similar, portable sills may be fitted on the following conditions:

   (a)   they shall be installed before the ship leaves port; and

   (b)   they shall be gasketed and fastened by closely spaced through bolts.

Regulation 13
Position of hatchways, doorways and ventilators

For the purpose of the regulations, two positions of hatchways, doorways and ventilators are defined as follows:

Position 1 – Upon exposed freeboard and raised quarterdecks, and upon exposed superstructure decks situated forward of a point located a quarter of the ship's length from the forward perpendicular.

[P88] Position 2 – Upon exposed superstructure decks situated abaft a quarter of the ship's length from the forward perpendicular and located at least one standard height of superstructure above the freeboard deck.

Upon exposed superstructure decks situated forward of a point located a quarter of the ship's length from the forward perpendicular and located at least two standard heights of superstructure above the freeboard deck.

Regulation 14
Cargo and other hatchways

[P88] **(1)**   The construction and means for securing the weathertightness of cargo and other hatchways in positions 1 and 2 shall be at least equivalent to the requirements of regulation 16, unless the application of regulation 15 to such hatchways is granted by the Administration.

(2)   Coamings and hatchway covers to exposed hatchways on decks above the superstructure deck shall comply with the requirements of the Administration.

[P88] Regulation 14-1
[P88] *Hatchway coamings*

[P88] **(1)**   The coamings of hatchways shall be of substantial construction in accordance with their position, and their height above the deck shall be at least as follows:

(a)   600 mm if in position 1; and

(b)   450 mm if in position 2.

[P88] **(2)**   In the case of hatchways which comply with regulation 16(2) through (5), the height of these coamings may be reduced, or the coamings omitted entirely, on condition that the Administration is satisfied that the safety of the ship is not thereby impaired in any sea conditions.

Regulation 15
Hatchways closed by portable covers and secured weathertight by tarpaulins and battening devices

Hatchway covers

[P88] **(1)**   The width of each bearing surface for hatchway covers shall be at least 65 mm.

[P88] **(2)**   Where covers are made of wood, the finished thickness shall be at least 60 mm in association with a span of not more than 1.5 m.

[P88] **(3)**   Where covers are made of mild steel the strength shall be calculated in accordance with the requirement of regulation 16(2) to (4) and the product of the maximum stress thus calculated and the factor 1.25 shall not exceed the minimum upper yield point strength of the material. They shall be so designed as to limit the deflection to not more than 0.0056 times the span under these loads.

Refer to the unified interpretation for regulations 15(4), (5), (6), (7) and 16 of the 1966 Convention

---

Portable beams

[P88] **(4)**   Where portable beams for supporting hatchway covers are made of mild steel, the strength shall be calculated with assumed loads not less than 3.5 t/m^2 on hatchways in position 1 and not less than 2.6 t/m^2 on hatchways in position 2 and the product of the maximum stress thus calculated and the factor 1.47 shall not exceed the minimum upper yield point strength of the material. They shall be so designed as to limit the deflection to not more than 0.0044 times the span under these loads.

Refer to the unified interpretation for regulations 15(4), (5), (6), (7) and 16 of the 1966 Convention

[P88] **(5)** The assumed loads on hatchways in position 1 may be reduced to 2 t/m² for ships 24 m in length and shall be not less than 3.5 t/m² for ships 100 m in length. The corresponding loads on hatchways in position 2 may be reduced to 1.5 t/m² and 2.6 t/m², respectively. In all cases, values at intermediate lengths shall be obtained by linear interpolation.

Refer to the unified interpretation for regulations 15(4), (5), (6), (7) and 16 of the 1966 Convention

Pontoon covers

[P88] **(6)** Where pontoon covers used in place of portable beams and covers are made of mild steel, the strength shall be calculated in accordance with the requirements of regulation 16(2) to (4) and the product of the maximum stress thus calculated and the factor 1.47 shall not exceed the minimum upper yield point strength of the material. They shall be so designed as to limit the deflection to not more than 0.0044 times the span. Mild steel plating forming the tops of covers shall be not less in thickness than 1% of the spacing of stiffeners or 6 mm if that be greater.

Refer to the unified interpretation for regulations 15(4), (5), (6), (7) and 16 of the 1966 Convention

[P88] **(7)** The strength and stiffness of covers made of materials other than mild steel shall be equivalent to those of mild steel to the satisfaction of the Administration.

Carriers or sockets

[P88] **(8)** Carriers or sockets for portable beams shall be of substantial construction, and shall provide means for the efficient fitting and securing of the beams. Where rolling types of beams are used, the arrangements shall ensure that the beams remain properly in position when the hatchway is closed.

Cleats

[P88] **(9)** Cleats shall be set to fit the taper of the wedges. They shall be at least 65 mm wide and spaced not more than 600 mm centre to centre; the cleats along each side or end shall be not more than 150 mm from the hatch corners.

Battens and wedges

[P88] **(10)** Battens and wedges shall be efficient and in good condition. Wedges shall be of tough wood or other equivalent material. They shall have a taper of not more than 1 in 6 and shall be not less than 13 mm thick at the toes.

123

Tarpaulins

P88 **(11)**   At least two layers of tarpaulin in good condition shall be provided for each hatchway in position 1 or 2. The tarpaulins shall be waterproof and of ample strength. They shall be of a material of at least an approved standard weight and quality.

Security of hatchway covers

P88 **(12)**   For all hatchways in position 1 or 2 steel bars or other equivalent means shall be provided in order efficiently and independently to secure each section of hatchway covers after the tarpaulins are battened down. Hatchway covers of more than 1.5 m in length shall be secured by at least two such securing appliances.

**Refer to the unified interpretation for regulation 15(13)
of the 1966 Convention**

Regulation 16

P88 *Hatchways closed by weathertight covers of steel or other
equivalent materials*

---

see also the unified interpretation

P88 **(1)**   All hatchways in position 1 and 2 shall be fitted with hatch covers of steel or other equivalent material. Except as provided in regulation 14(2), such covers shall be weathertight and fitted with gaskets and clamping devices. The means for securing and maintaining weathertightness shall be to the satisfaction of the Administration. The arrangements shall ensure that the tightness can be maintained in any sea conditions, and for this purpose tests for tightness shall be required at the initial survey, and may be required at renewal and annual surveys or at more frequent intervals.

P88 *Hatch cover minimum design loads*

P88 **(2)**   For ships of 100 m in length and above:

(a)   Position 1 hatch covers located in the forward quarter of the ship's length shall be designed for wave loads at the forward perpendicular, calculated from the following equation:

$$\text{Load} = 5 + (L_H - 100)a \quad \text{in t/m}^2$$

where:

L_H is L for ships of not more than 340 m but not less than 100 m in length and equal to 340 m for ships of more than 340 m in length;

L is the length of the ship (metres), as defined in regulation 3;

a is given in table 16.1,

and reduced linearly to 3.5 t/m^2 at the end of the forward quarter's length, as shown in table 16.2. The design load used for each hatch cover panel shall be that determined at its midpoint location.

(b)   All other position 1 hatch covers shall be designed to 3.5 t/m^2.

P88 **Table 16.1**

	a
Type 'B' freeboard ships	0.0074
Ships assigned reduced freeboard by regulation 27(9) or (10)	0.0363

(c) Position 2 hatch covers shall be designed to 2.6 t/m^2.

(d) Where a position 1 hatchway is located at least one superstructure standard height higher than the freeboard deck, it may be designed to 3.5 t/m^2.

P88 **(3)** For ships 24 m in length:

(a) Position 1 hatch covers located in the forward quarter of the ship's length shall be designed for wave loads of 2.43 t/m^2 at the forward perpendicular and reduced linearly to 2 t/m^2 at the end of the forward quarter's length as shown in table 16.2. The design load used for each hatch cover panel shall be that determined at its midpoint location.

(b) All other position 1 hatch covers shall be designed to 2 t/m^2.

(c) Position 2 hatch covers shall be designed to 1.5 t/m^2.

(d) Where a position 1 hatchway is located at least one superstructure standard height higher than the freeboard deck, it may be designed to 2 t/m^2.

P88 **(4)** For ships between 24 m and 100 m in length, and for positions between F.P. and 0.25L, wave loads shall be obtained by linear interpolation of the values shown in table 16.2.

P88 **Table 16.2**

	Longitudinal position		
	F.P.	**0.25L**	**Aft of 0.25L**
$L > 100$ m			
Freeboard deck	Equation in 16(2)(a)	3.5 t/m^2	3.5 t/m^2
Superstructure deck	3.5 t/m^2		2.6 t/m^2
$L = 100$ m			
Freeboard deck	5 t/m^2	3.5 t/m^2	3.5 t/m^2
Superstructure deck	3.5 t/m^2		2.6 t/m^2
$L = 24$ m			
Freeboard deck	2.43 t/m^2	2 t/m^2	2 t/m^2
Superstructure deck	2 t/m^2		1.5 t/m^2

P88 **(5)** All hatch covers shall be designed such that:

(a) the product of the maximum stress determined in accordance with the above loads and the factor of 1.25 does not exceed the minimum upper yield point strength of the material in tension and the critical buckling strength in compression;

(b) the deflection is limited to not more than 0.0056 times the span;

(c) steel plating forming the tops of covers is not less in thickness than 1% of the spacing of stiffeners or 6 mm if that be greater; and

(d) an appropriate corrosion margin is incorporated.

P88 *Securing arrangements*

P88 **(6)** The means for securing and maintaining weathertightness by other means than gaskets and clamping shall be to the satisfaction of the Administration.

P88 **(7)** Hatch covers which rest on coamings shall be located in their closed position by means capable of withstanding horizontally acting loads in any sea conditions.

Regulation 17
Machinery space openings

(1) Machinery space openings in position 1 or 2 shall be properly framed and efficiently enclosed by steel casings of ample strength, and where the casings are not protected by other structures their strength shall be specially considered. Access openings in such casings shall be fitted with doors complying with the requirements of regulation 12(1), the sills of which shall be at least 600 mm above the deck if in position 1, and at least 380 mm above the deck if in position 2. Other openings in such casings shall be fitted with equivalent covers, permanently attached in their proper positions.

P88 **(2)** Where machinery casings are not protected by other structures, double doors (i.e. inner and outer doors complying with the requirements of regulation 12(1)) shall be required for ships assigned freeboards less than those based on table 28.2 of regulation 28. An inner sill of 230 mm in conjunction with the outer sill of 600 mm shall be provided.

P88 **(3)** Coamings of any fiddley, funnel or machinery space ventilator in an exposed position on the freeboard deck or superstructure deck shall be as high above the deck as is reasonable and practicable. In general, ventilators necessary to continuously supply the machinery space shall have coamings of sufficient height to comply with regulation 19(3), without having to fit weathertight closing appliances. Ventilators necessary to continuously supply the emergency generator room, if this is considered buoyant in the stability calculation, or protecting openings leading below shall have coamings of sufficient height to comply with regulation 19(3), without having to fit weathertight closing appliances.

[P88] **(4)**   Where due to ship size and arrangement this is not practicable, lesser heights for machinery space and emergency generator room ventilator coamings, fitted with weathertight closing appliances in accordance with regulation 19(4), may be permitted by the Administration in combination with other suitable arrangements to ensure an uninterrupted, adequate supply of ventilation to these spaces.

[P88] **(5)**   Fiddley openings shall be fitted with strong covers of steel or other equivalent material permanently attached in their proper positions and capable of being secured weathertight.

Regulation 18
Miscellaneous openings in freeboard and
superstructure decks

(1)   Manholes and flush scuttles in position 1 or 2 or within superstructures other than enclosed superstructures shall be closed by substantial covers capable of being made watertight. Unless secured by closely spaced bolts, the covers shall be permanently attached.

[P88] **(2)**   Openings in freeboard decks other than hatchways, machinery space openings, manholes and flush scuttles shall be protected by an enclosed superstructure, or by a deckhouse or companionway of equivalent strength and weathertightness. Similarly, any such opening in an exposed super-structure deck, in the top of a deckhouse on the freeboard deck which gives access to a space below the freeboard deck or a space within an enclosed superstructure shall be protected by an efficient deckhouse or companionway. Doorways in such companionways or deckhouses that lead or give access to stairways leading below shall be fitted with doors in accordance with regulation 12(1). Alternatively, if stairways within a deckhouse are enclosed within properly constructed companionways fitted with doors complying with regulation 12(1), the external door need not be weathertight.

see also the unified interpretation *(IACS interpretation LL.8)*

[P88] **(3)**   Openings in the top of a deckhouse on a raised quarterdeck or superstructure of less than standard height, having a height equal to or greater than the standard quarterdeck height, shall be provided with an acceptable means of closing but need not be protected by an efficient deckhouse or companionway as defined in the regulation, provided that the height of the deckhouse is at least the standard height of a superstructure. Openings in the top of the deckhouse on a deckhouse of less than a standard superstructure height may be treated in a similar manner.

[P88] **(4)**   In position 1 the height above the deck of sills to the doorways in companionways shall be at least 600 mm. In position 2 it shall be at least 380 mm.

[P88] **(5)**   Where access is provided from the deck above as an alternative to access from the freeboard deck in accordance with regulation 3(10)(b), the height of sills into a bridge or poop shall be 380 mm. The same shall apply to deckhouses on the freeboard deck.

[P88] **(6)** Where access is not provided from above, the height of the sills to doorways in deckhouses on the freeboard deck shall be 600 mm.

Refer to the unified interpretation for regulation 18(3) of the 1966 Convention

[P88] **(7)** Where the closing appliances of access openings in superstructures and deckhouses are not in accordance with regulation 12(1), interior deck openings shall be considered exposed (i.e. situated in the open deck).

Regulation 19
Ventilators

see also the unified interpretation

[P88] **(1)** Ventilators in position 1 or 2 to spaces below freeboard deck or decks of enclosed superstructures shall have coamings of steel or other equivalent material, substantially constructed and efficiently connected to the deck. Ventilators in position 1 shall have coamings of a height of at least 900 mm above the deck; in position 2 the coamings shall be of a height at least 760 mm above the deck. Where the coaming of any ventilator exceeds 900 mm in height it shall be specially supported.

(2) Ventilators passing through superstructures other than enclosed superstructures shall have substantially constructed coamings of steel or other equivalent material at the freeboard deck.

(3) Ventilators in position 1 the coamings of which extend to more than 4.5 m above the deck, and in position 2 the coamings of which extend to more than 2.3 m above the deck, need not be fitted with closing arrangements unless specifically required by the Administration.

[P88] **(4)** Except as provided in paragraph (3), ventilator openings shall be provided with weathertight closing appliances of steel or other equivalent material. In ships of not more than 100 m in length the closing appliances shall be permanently attached; where not so provided in other ships, they shall be conveniently stowed near the ventilators to which they are to be fitted.

[P88] **(5)** In exposed locations, the height of coamings may be increased to the satisfaction of the Administration.

Regulation 20
Air pipes

see also the unified interpretations

[P88] **(1)** Where air pipes to ballast and other tanks extend above the freeboard or superstructure decks, the exposed parts of the pipes shall be of substantial construction; the height from the deck to the point where water may have access below shall be at least 760 mm on the freeboard deck and 450 mm on the superstructure deck.

[P88] **(2)**   Where these heights may interfere with the working of the ship, a lower height may be approved, provided that the Administration is satisfied that the closing arrangements and other circumstances justify a lower height.

[P88] **(3)**   Air pipes shall be provided with automatic closing devices.

[P88] **(4)**   Pressure–vacuum valves (PV valves) may be accepted on tankers.

Regulation 21
Cargo ports and other similar openings

see also the unified interpretation

[P88] **(1)**   Cargo ports and other similar openings in the sides of ships below the freeboard deck shall be fitted with doors so designed as to ensure the same watertightness and structural integrity as the surrounding shell plating. Unless otherwise granted by the Administration, these openings shall open outwards. The number of such openings shall be the minimum compatible with the design and proper working of the ship.

see also the unified interpretation

[P88] **(2)**   Unless otherwise permitted by the Administration, the lower edge of openings referred to in paragraph (1) shall not be below a line drawn parallel to the freeboard deck at side, which is at its lowest point at least 230 mm above the upper edge of the uppermost load line.

[P88] **(3)**   Where it is permitted to arrange cargo ports and other similar openings with their lower edge below the line specified in paragraph (2), additional features shall be fitted to maintain the watertight integrity.

[P88] **(4)**   The fitting of a second door of equivalent strength and watertightness is one acceptable arrangement. A leakage detection device shall be provided in the compartment between the two doors. Drainage of this compartment to the bilges, controlled by a readily accessible screw-down valve, shall be arranged. The outer door shall open outwards.

[P88] **(5)**   Arrangements for bow doors and their inner doors, side doors and stern doors and their securings shall be in compliance with the requirements of a recognized organization, or with the applicable national standards of the Administration which provide an equivalent level of safety.

Regulation 22
Scuppers, inlets and discharges

see also the unified interpretation

[P88] **(1)**   **(a)** Discharges led through the shell either from spaces below the freeboard deck or from within superstructures and deckhouses on the freeboard deck fitted with doors complying with the requirements of regulation 12 shall, except as provided in paragraph (2), be fitted with efficient and accessible means for preventing water from passing inboard. Normally each separate discharge shall have one automatic non-return valve with a positive means of closing it from a position above the freeboard deck.

Where the inboard end of the discharge pipe is located at least 0.01L above the Summer Load Line, the discharge may have two automatic non-return valves without positive means of closing. Where that vertical distance exceeds 0.02L, a single automatic non-return valve without positive means of closing may be accepted. The means for operating the positive-action valve shall be readily accessible and provided with an indicator showing whether the valve is open or closed.

P88 **(b)** One automatic non-return valve and one sluice valve controlled from above the freeboard deck instead of one automatic non-return valve with a positive means of closing from a position above the freeboard deck, is acceptable.

P88 **(c)** Where two automatic non-return valves are required, the inboard valve shall always be accessible for examination under service conditions (i.e., the inboard valve shall be above the level of the Tropical Load Line). If this is not practicable, the inboard valve need not be located above the Tropical Load Line, provided that a locally controlled sluice valve is fitted between the two automatic non-return valves.

P88 **(d)** Where sanitary discharges and scuppers lead overboard through the shell in way of machinery spaces, a locally operated positive-closing valve at the shell, together with a non-return valve inboard, is acceptable. The controls of the valves shall be in an easily accessible position.

P88 **(e)** The position of the inboard end of discharges shall be related to the Summer Timber Load Line when a timber freeboard is assigned.

P88 **(f)** The requirements for non-return valves are applicable only to those discharges which remain open during the normal operation of a ship. For discharges which are to be kept closed at sea, a single screw-down valve operated from the deck is acceptable.

P88 **(g)** Table 22.1 provides the acceptable arrangements of scuppers, inlets and discharges.

P88 **(2)** Scuppers led through the shell from enclosed superstructures used for the carriage of cargo shall be permitted only where the edge of the freeboard deck is not immersed when the ship heels 5° either way. In other cases the drainage shall be led inboard in accordance with the requirements of the International Convention for the Safety of Life at Sea in force.

P88 **(3)** In manned machinery spaces, main and auxiliary sea inlets and discharges in connection with the operation of machinery may be controlled locally. The controls shall be readily accessible and shall be provided with indicators showing whether the valves are open or closed.

P88 **(4)** Scuppers and discharge pipes originating at any level and penetrating the shell either more than 450 mm below the freeboard deck or less than 600 mm above the Summer Load Line shall be provided with a non-return valve at the shell. This valve, unless required by paragraph (2), may be omitted if the piping is of substantial thickness (see paragraph (7) below).

P88 **Table 22.1**

Discharges coming from enclosed spaces below the freeboard deck or on the freeboard deck

Discharges coming from other spaces

General requirement Reg. 22(1) where inboard end ≤ 0.01L above SWL	Discharges through machinery space	Alternatives (Reg. 22(1)) where inboard end		Outboard end > 450 mm below FB deck or ≤ 600 mm above SWL Reg. 22(4)	Otherwise Reg. 22(5)
		> 0.01L above SWL	> 0.02L above SWL		

Superstructure or deckhouse deck

FB deck

SWL

TWL

Symbols:

▽ inboard end of pipes

⅄ outboard end of pipes

pipes terminating on the open deck

⊘ Non-return valve without positive means of closing

Non-return valve with positive means of closing controlled locally

⊠ valve controlled locally

remote control

normal thickness

substantial thickness

131

P88 **(5)** Scuppers leading from superstructures or deckhouses not fitted with doors complying with the requirements of regulation 12 shall be led overboard.

P88 **(6)** All shell fittings and the valves required by this regulation shall be of steel, bronze or other approved ductile material. Valves of ordinary cast iron or similar material are not acceptable. All pipes to which this regulation refers shall be of steel or other equivalent material to the satisfaction of the Administration.

P88 **(7)** ***Scupper and discharge pipes***

P88 **(a)** For scupper and discharge pipes, where substantial thickness is not required:

(i) for pipes having an external diameter equal to or less than 155 mm, the thickness shall not be less than 4.5 mm;

(ii) for pipes having an external diameter equal to or more than 230 mm, the thickness shall not be less than 6 mm.

Intermediate sizes shall be determined by linear interpolation.

P88 **(b)** For scupper and discharge pipes, where substantial thickness is required:

(i) for pipes having an external diameter equal to or less than 80 mm, the thickness shall not be less than 7 mm;

(ii) for pipes having an external diameter of 180 mm, the thickness shall not be less than 10 mm;

(iii) for pipes having an external diameter equal to or more than 220 mm, the thickness shall not be less than 12.5 mm.

Intermediate sizes shall be determined by linear interpolation.

P88 Regulation 22-1
P88 *Garbage chutes*

Refer to the unified interpretation for regulation 22 of the 1966 Convention

---

P88 **(1)** Two gate valves controlled from the working deck of the chute instead of the non-return valve with a positive means of closing from a position above the freeboard deck which comply with the following requirements are acceptable:

(a) the lower gate valve shall be controlled from a position above the freeboard deck. An interlock system between the two valves shall be arranged;

(b) the inboard end shall be located above the waterline formed by an 8.5° heel to port or starboard at a draught corresponding to the assigned summer freeboard, but not less than 1,000 mm above the summer waterline. Where the inboard end exceeds $0.01L$ above the summer waterline, valve control from the freeboard deck is not required, provided the inboard gate valve is always accessible under service conditions; and

(c) alternatively, the upper and lower gate valves may be replaced by a hinged weathertight cover at the inboard end of the chute together with a discharge flap. The cover and flap shall be arranged with an interlock so that the discharge flap cannot be operated until the hopper cover is closed.

P88 **(2)** The entire chute, including the cover, shall be constructed of material of substantial thickness.

P88 **(3)** The controls for the gate valves and/or hinged covers shall be clearly marked: "Keep closed when not in use".

P88 **(4)** Where the inboard end of the chute is below the freeboard deck of a passenger ship or the equilibrium waterlines of a cargo ship to which damage stability requirements apply, then:

(a) the inboard end hinged cover/valve shall be watertight;

(b) the valve shall be a screw-down non-return valve fitted in an easily accessible position above the deepest load line; and

(c) the screw-down non-return valve shall be controlled from a position above the bulkhead deck and provided with open/closed indicators. The valve control shall be clearly marked: "Keep closed when not in use".

P88 Regulation 22-2
P88 *Spurling pipes and cable lockers*

P88 **(1)** Spurling pipes and cable lockers shall be watertight up to the deck exposed to weather.

P88 **(2)** Where means of access are provided, they shall be closed by a substantial cover and secured by closely spaced bolts.

P88 **(3)** Spurling pipes through which anchor cables are led shall be provided with permanently attached closing appliances to minimize water ingress.

Regulation 23
P88 *Sidescuttles, windows and skylights*

P88 **(1)** Sidescuttles and windows, together with their glasses, deadlights and storm covers*, if fitted, shall be of an approved design and substantial construction. Non-metallic frames are not acceptable.

P88 **(2)** Sidescuttles are defined as being round or oval openings with an area not exceeding 0.16 m^2. Round or oval openings having areas exceeding 0.16 m^2 shall be treated as windows.

P88 **(3)** Windows are defined as being rectangular openings generally, having a radius at each corner relative to the window size, and round or oval openings with an area exceeding 0.16 m^2.

---

* Deadlights are fitted to the inside of windows and sidescuttles, while storm covers are fitted to the outside of windows, where accessible, and may be hinged or portable.

[P88] **(4)**   Sidescuttles to the following spaces shall be fitted with hinged inside deadlights:

(a)   spaces below freeboard deck;

(b)   spaces within the first tier of enclosed superstructures; and

(c)   first tier deckhouses on the freeboard deck protecting openings leading below or considered buoyant in stability calculations.

[P88] Deadlights shall be capable of being closed and secured watertight if fitted below the freeboard deck and weathertight if fitted above.

[P88] **(5)**   Sidescuttles shall not be fitted in such a position that their sills are below a line drawn parallel to the freeboard deck at side and having its lowest point 2.5% of the breadth (*B*), or 500 mm, whichever is the greater distance, above the Summer Load Line (or Timber Summer Load Line if assigned).

[P88] **(6)** If the required damage stability calculations indicate that the sidescuttles would become immersed at any intermediate stage of flooding or the final equilibrium waterline, they shall be of the non-opening type.

[P88] **(7)**   Windows shall not be fitted in the following locations:

(a)   below the freeboard deck;

(b)   in the first tier end bulkheads or sides of enclosed superstructures; or

(c)   in first tier deckhouses that are considered buoyant in the stability calculations.

---
see also the unified interpretation *(IACS interpretation LL.62)*

[P88] **(8)**   Sidescuttles and windows at the side shell in the second tier shall be provided with hinged inside deadlights capable of being closed and secured weathertight if the superstructure protects direct access to an opening leading below or is considered buoyant in the stability calculations.

[P88] **(9)**   Sidescuttles and windows in side bulkheads set inboard from the side shell in the second tier which protect direct access below to spaces listed in paragraph (4) shall be provided with either hinged inside deadlights or, where they are accessible, permanently attached external storm covers which are capable of being closed and secured weathertight.

[P88] **(10)**   Cabin bulkheads and doors in the second tier and above separating sidescuttles and windows from a direct access leading below or the second tier considered buoyant in the stability calculations may be accepted in place of deadlights or storm covers fitted to the sidescuttles and windows.

---
see also the unified interpretation *(IACS interpretation LL.62)*

[P88] **(11)**   Deckhouses situated on a raised quarterdeck or on the deck of a superstructure of less than standard height may be regarded as being in the second tier as far as the requirements for deadlights are concerned, provided that the height of the raised quarterdeck or superstructure is equal to or greater than the standard quarterdeck height.

[P88] **(12)**   Fixed or opening skylights shall have a glass thickness appropriate to their size and position as required for sidescuttles and windows. Skylight glasses in any position shall be protected from mechanical damage and, where fitted in position 1 or 2, shall be provided with permanently attached deadlights or storm covers.

Regulation 24
Freeing ports

`P88` **(1)** **(a)** Where bulwarks on the weather portions of freeboard or super-structure decks form wells, ample provision shall be made for rapidly freeing the decks of water and for draining them.

`P88` **(b)** Except as provided in paragraphs (1)(c) and (2), the minimum freeing port area (A) on each side of the ship for each well on the freeboard deck shall be that given by the following formulae in cases where the sheer in way of the well is standard or greater than standard.

`P88` The minimum area for each well on superstructure decks shall be one-half of the area given by the following formulae:

Where the length of bulwark (l) in the well is 20 m or less:
$$A = 0.7 + 0.035l \text{ m}^2.$$

Where l exceeds 20 m:
$$A = 0.07l \text{ m}^2.$$

l need in no case be taken as greater than 0.7L.

If the bulwark is more than 1.2 m in average height, the required area shall be increased by 0.004 m^2 per metre of length of well for each 0.1 m difference in height. If the bulwark is less than 0.9 m in average height, the required area may be decreased by 0.004 m^2 per metre of length of well for each 0.1 m difference in height.

---
see also the unified interpretations

`P88` **(c)** In ships with no sheer, the area calculated according to paragraph (b) shall be increased by 50%. Where the sheer is less than the standard, the percentage shall be obtained by linear interpolation.

`P88` **(d)** On a flush deck ship with a deckhouse amidships having a breadth of at least 80% of the beam of the ship and the passageways along the side of the ship not exceeding 1.5 m in width, two wells are formed. Each shall be given the required freeing port area based upon the length of each well.

`P88` **(e)** Where a screen bulkhead is fitted completely across the ship at the forward end of a midship deckhouse, the exposed deck is divided into two wells and there is no limitation on the breadth of the deckhouse.

`P88` **(f)** Wells on raised quarterdecks shall be treated as being on freeboard decks.

`P88` **(g)** Gutter bars greater than 300 mm in height fitted around the weather decks of tankers in way of cargo manifolds and cargo piping shall be treated as bulwarks. Freeing ports shall be arranged in accordance with this regulation. Closures attached to the freeing ports for use during loading and discharge operations are to be arranged in such a way that jamming cannot occur while at sea.

P88 **(2)**   Where a ship fitted with a trunk does not comply with the requirements of regulation 36(1)(e) or where continuous or substantially continuous hatchway side coamings are fitted between detached super-structures, the minimum area of the freeing port openings shall be calculated from the following table:

Breadth of hatchway or trunk in relation to the breadth of ship	Area of freeing ports in relation to the total area of the bulwarks
40% or less	20%
75% or more	10%

The area of freeing ports at intermediate breadths shall be obtained by linear interpolation.

P88 **(3)**   The effectiveness of the freeing area in bulwarks required by paragraph (1) depends on the free flow area across the deck of a ship.

P88 The free flow area on deck is the net area of gaps between hatchways, and between hatchways and superstructures and deckhouses up to the actual height of the bulwark.

P88 The freeing port area in bulwarks shall be assessed in relation to the net free flow area as follows:

(a)   If the free flow area is not less than the freeing area calculated from paragraph (2) as if the hatchway coamings were continuous, then the minimum freeing port area calculated from paragraph (1) shall be deemed sufficient.

(b)   If the free flow area is equal to or less than the area calculated from paragraph (1), the minimum freeing area in the bulwarks shall be determined from paragraph (2).

(c)   If the free flow area is smaller than calculated from paragraph (2), but greater than calculated from paragraph (1), the minimum freeing area in the bulwark shall be determined from the following formula:

$$F = F_1 + F_2 - f_p \ (\text{m}^2)$$

where:

F_1 is the minimum freeing area calculated from paragraph (1);

F_2 is the minimum freeing area calculated from paragraph (2); and

f_p is the total net area of passages and gaps between hatch ends and superstructures or deckhouses up to the actual height of bulwark.

P88 **(4)**   In ships having superstructures on the freeboard deck or superstructure decks, which are open at either or both ends to wells formed by bulwarks on the open decks, adequate provision for freeing the open spaces within the superstructures shall be provided.

[P88] The minimum freeing port area on each side of the ship for the open superstructure (A_s) and for the open well (A_w) shall be calculated in accordance with the following procedure:

(a) Determine the total well length (l_t) equal to the sum of the length of the open deck enclosed by bulwarks (l_w) and the length of the common space within the open superstructure (l_s).

(b) To determine A_s:

    (i) calculate the freeing port area (A) required for an open well of length l_t in accordance with paragraph (1) with standard height bulwark assumed;

    (ii) multiply by a factor of 1.5 to correct for the absence of sheer, if applicable, in accordance with paragraph (1)(c);

    (iii) multiply by the factor (b_o/l_t) to adjust the freeing port area for the breadth (b_o) of the openings in the end bulkhead of the enclosed superstructure;

    (iv) to adjust the freeing port area for that part of the entire length of the well which is enclosed by the open superstructure, multiply by the factor:

$$1 - (l_w/l_t)^2$$

    where l_w and l_t are defined in paragraph (4)(a).

    (v) to adjust the freeing port area for the distance of the well deck above the freeboard deck, for decks located more than $0.5h_s$ above the freeboard deck, multiply by the factor:

$$0.5(h_s/h_w)$$

    where h_w is the distance of the well deck above the freeboard deck and h_s is one standard superstructure height.

(c) To determine A_w:

    (i) the freeing port area for the open well (A_w) shall be calculated in accordance with paragraph (b)(i), using l_w to calculate a nominal freeing port area (A'), and then adjusted for the actual height of the bulwark (h_b) by the application of one of the following area corrections, whichever is applicable:

    for bulwarks greater than 1.2 m in height:

$$A_c = l_w((h_b - 1.2)/0.10)(0.004) \ (\text{m}^2);$$

    for bulwarks less than 0.9 m in height:

$$A_c = l_w((h_b - 0.9)/0.10)(0.004) \ (\text{m}^2);$$

    for bulwarks between 1.2 m and 0.9 m in height there is no correction (i.e. $A_c = 0$);

    (ii) the corrected freeing port area $(A_w = A' + A_c)$ shall then be adjusted for absence of sheer, if applicable, and height above freeboard deck as in paragraphs (b)(ii) and (b)(v), using h_s and h_w.

(d) The resulting freeing port areas for the open superstructure (A_s) and for the open well (A_w) shall be provided along each side of the open space covered by the open superstructure and each side of the open well, respectively.

(e) The above relationships are summarized by the following equations, assuming l_t, the sum of l_w and l_s, is greater than 20 m:

freeing port area A_w for the open well:

$$A_w = (0.07l_w + A_c) \text{ (sheer correction) } (0.5h_s/h_w);$$

freeing port area A_s for the open superstructure:

$$A_s = (0.07l_t) \text{ (sheer correction) } (b_o/l_t) (1 - (l_w/l_t)^2) (0.5h_s/h_w);$$

where l_t is 20 m or less, the basic freeing port area is $A = 0.7 + 0.035l_t$ in accordance with paragraph (1).

P88 (5) The lower edges of freeing ports shall be as near the deck as practicable. Two-thirds of the freeing port area required shall be provided in the half of the well nearest the lowest point of the sheer curve. One-third of the freeing port area required shall be evenly spread along the remaining length of the well. With zero or little sheer on the exposed freeboard deck or an exposed superstructure deck the freeing port area shall be evenly spread along the length of the well.

P88 (6) All freeing port openings in the bulwarks shall be protected by rails or bars spaced approximately 230 mm apart. If shutters are fitted to freeing ports, ample clearance shall be provided to prevent jamming. Hinges shall have pins or bearings of non-corrodible material. Shutters shall not be fitted with securing appliances.

Regulation 25
Protection of the crew

P88 (1) The deckhouses used for the accommodation of the crew shall be constructed to an acceptable level of strength.

P88 (2) Guard rails or bulwarks shall be fitted around all exposed decks. The height of the bulwarks or guard rails shall be at least 1 m from the deck, provided that, where this height would interfere with the normal operation of the ship, a lesser height may be approved, if the Administration is satisfied that adequate protection is provided.

see also the unified interpretation *(IACS interpretation LL.14)*

P88 (3) Guard rails fitted on superstructure and freeboard decks shall have at least three courses. The opening below the lowest course of the guard rails shall not exceed 230 mm. The other courses shall be not more than 380 mm apart. In the case of ships with rounded gunwales the guard rail supports shall be placed on the flat of the deck. In other locations, guard rails with at least two courses shall be fitted. Guard rails shall comply with the following provisions:

(a) fixed, removable or hinged stanchions shall be fitted about 1.5 m apart. Removable or hinged stanchions shall be capable of being locked in the upright position;

(b) at least every third stanchion shall be supported by a bracket or stay;

(c)   where necessary for the normal operation of the ship, steel wire ropes may be accepted in lieu of guard rails. Wires shall be made taut by means of turnbuckles; and

(d)   where necessary for the normal operation of the ship, chains fitted between two fixed stanchions and/or bulwarks are acceptable in lieu of guard rails.

[P88] **(4)**   Satisfactory means for safe passage required by regulation 25-1 (in the form of guard rails, lifelines, gangways or underdeck passages, etc.) shall be provided for the protection of the crew in getting to and from their quarters, the machinery space and any other spaces used in the essential operation of the ship.

[P88] **(5)**   Deck cargo carried on any ship shall be so stowed that any opening which is in way of the cargo and which gives access to and from the crew's quarters, the machinery space and all other parts used in the essential operation of the ship can be closed and secured against water ingress. Protection for the crew in the form of guard rails or lifelines shall be provided above the deck cargo if there is no convenient passage on or below the deck of the ship.

[P88] Regulation 25-1
[P88] *Means for safe passage of crew*

[P88] **(1)**   The safe passage of crew shall be provided by at least one of the means prescribed in table 25-1.1 below.

[P88] **(2)**   Acceptable arrangements referred to in table 25-1.1 are defined as follows:

(a)   A well lighted and ventilated under-deck passageway (with a clear opening of at least 0.8 m wide and 2 m high), as close as practicable to the freeboard deck, connecting and providing access to the locations in question.

(b)   A permanent and efficiently constructed gangway, fitted at or above the level of the superstructure deck, on or as near as practicable to the centreline of the ship, providing a continuous platform at least 0.6 m in width and a non-slip surface and with guard rails extending on each side throughout its length. Guard rails shall be at least 1 m high with three courses and constructed as required in regulation 25(3). A foot-stop shall be provided.

(c)   A permanent walkway at least 0.6 m in width, fitted at freeboard deck level and consisting of two rows of guard rails with stanchions spaced not more than 3 m. The number of courses of rails and their spacing shall be in accordance with regulation 25(3). On type 'B' ships, hatchway coamings not less than 0.6 m in height may be accepted as forming one side of the walkway, provided that two rows of guard rails are fitted between the hatchways.

(d)   A wire rope lifeline not less than 10 mm in diameter, supported by stanchions not more than 10 m apart, or a single handrail or wire rope attached to hatch coamings, continued and supported between hatchways.

Table 25-1.1

Type of ship	Locations of access in ship	Assigned summer freeboard	Acceptable arrangements according to type of freeboard assigned[‡]			
			Type 'A'	Type 'B-100'	Type 'B-60'	Type 'B' and 'B+'
All ships other than oil tankers*, chemical tanker* and gas carriers*	1.1 *Access to midship quarters* 1.1.1 Between poop and bridge, or	⩽ 3000 mm	(a) (b) (e)	(a) (b) (e)	(a) (b) (c)(i) (e) (f)(i)	(a) (b) (c)(i) (c)(ii) (c)(iv) (d)(i) (d)(ii) (d)(iii) (e) (f)(i) (f)(ii) (f)(iv)
	1.1.2 Between poop and deckhouse containing living accommodation or navigating equipment, or both	> 3000 mm	(a) (b) (e)	(a) (b) (e)	(a) (b) (c)(i) (c)(ii) (e) (f)(i) (f)(ii)	
	1.2 *Access to ends* 1.2.1 Between poop and bow (if there is no bridge), 1.2.2 Between bridge and bow, or	⩽ 3000 mm	(a) (b) (c)(i) (e) (f)(i)	(a) (b) (c)(i) (c)(ii) (e) (f)(i) (f)(ii)	(a) (b) (c)(i) (c)(ii) (e) (f)(i) (f)(ii)	
	1.2.3 Between a deckhouse containing living accommodation or navigating equipment, or both, and bow, or 1.2.4 In the case of a flush deck ship, between crew accommodation and the forward and after ends of ship	> 3000 mm	(a) (b) (c)(i) (d)(i) (e) (f)(i)	(a) (b) (c)(i) (c)(ii) (d)(i) (d)(ii) (e) (f)(i) (f)(ii)	(a) (b) (c)(i) (c)(ii) (c)(iv) (d)(i) (d)(ii) (d)(iii) (e) (f)(i) (f)(ii) (f)(iv)	

* Oil tankers, chemical tankers and gas carriers as defined in regulations II-1/2.12, VII/8.2 and VII/11.2, respectively, of the International Convention for the Safety of Life at Sea, in force.

‡ Arrangements (a) - (f) are described in paragraph (2) below. Locations (i) - (v) are described in paragraph (3) below.

Table 25-1.1 *(continued)*

Type of ship	Locations of access in ship	Assigned summer freeboard	Acceptable arrangements according to type of freeboard assigned[‡]
			Type A
Oil tankers*, chemical tankers* and gas carriers*	2.1 *Access to bow* 2.1.1 Between poop and bow or 2.1.2 Between a deck-house containing living accommodation or navigating equipment, or both, and bow, or 2.1.3 In the case of a flush deck ship, between crew accommodation and the forward end of ship.	$\leqslant (A_f + H_s)^{\dagger}$ $> (A_f + H_s)^{\dagger}$	(a) (e) (f)(i) (f)(v) (a) (e) (f)(i) (f)(ii)
	2.2 *Access to after end* In the case of a flush deck ship, between crew accommodation and the after end of ship	as required in 1.2.4 for other types of ships	

* Oil tankers, chemical tankers and gas carriers as defined in regulations II-1/2.12, VII/8.2 and VII/11.2, respectively, of the International Convention for the Safety of Life at Sea, in force.

[†] A_f: the minimum summer freeboard calculated as type 'A' ship regardless of the type freeboard actually assigned.

H_s: the standard height of superstructure as defined in regulation 33.

[‡] Arrangements (a) - (f) are described in paragraph (2) below. Locations (i) - (v) are described in paragraph (3) below.

(e) A permanent gangway that is:

(i) located at or above the level of the superstructure deck;

(ii) located on or as near as practicable to the centreline of the ship;

(iii) located so as not to hinder easy access across the working areas of the deck;

(iv) providing a continuous platform at least 1 m in width;

(v) constructed of fire-resistant and non-slip material;

(vi) fitted with guard rails extending on each side throughout its length; guard rails shall be at least 1 m high with courses as required by regulation 25(3) and supported by stanchions spaced not more than 1.5 m apart;

(vii) provided with a foot-stop on each side;

(viii) having openings, with ladders where appropriate, to and from the deck. Openings shall not be more than 40 m apart; and

(ix) having shelters set in way of the gangway at intervals not exceeding 45 m if the length of the exposed deck to be traversed exceeds 70 m. Every such shelter shall be capable of accommodating at least one person and be so constructed as to afford weather protection on the forward, port and starboard sides.

(f) A permanent walkway located at the freeboard deck level, on or as near as practicable to the centreline of the ship, having the same specifications as those for a permanent gangway listed in (e), except for foot-stops. On type 'B' ships (certified for the carriage of liquids in bulk) with a combined height of hatch coaming and fitted hatch cover of not less than 1 m in height, the hatchway coamings may be accepted as forming one side of the walkway, provided that two rows of guard rails are fitted between the hatchways.

P88 **(3)** Permitted transverse locations for arrangements in paragraphs (2)(c), (d) and (f) above, where appropriate:

(i) at or near the centreline of the ship; or fitted on hatchways at or near the centreline of the ship;

(ii) fitted on each side of the ship;

(iii) fitted on one side of the ship, provision being made for fitting on either side;

(iv) fitted on one side of the ship only;

(v) fitted on each side of the hatchways, as near to the centreline as practicable.

P88 **(4)** **(a)** Where wire ropes are fitted, turnbuckles shall be provided to ensure their tautness.

P88 **(b)** Where necessary for the normal operation of the ship, steel wire ropes may be accepted in lieu of guard rails.

P88 **(c)** Where necessary for the normal operation of the ship, chains fitted between two fixed stanchions are acceptable in lieu of guard rails.

P88 **(d)** Where stanchions are fitted, every third stanchion shall be supported by a bracket or stay.

P88 **(e)** Removable or hinged stanchions shall be capable of being locked in the upright position.

P88 **(f)** A means of passage over obstructions such as pipes or other fittings of a permanent nature shall be provided.

P88 **(g)** Generally, the width of the gangway or deck-level walkway should not exceed 1.5 m.

P88 **(5)** For tankers less than 100 m in length, the minimum width of the gangway platform or deck-level walkway fitted in accordance with paragraphs (2)(e) or (f) above, respectively, may be reduced to 0.6 m.

Regulation 26
Special conditions of assignment for type 'A' ships

see also the unified interpretation

Machinery casings

P88 **(1)**   Machinery casings on type 'A' ships, as defined in regulation 27, shall be protected by one of the following arrangements:

(a)   an enclosed poop or bridge of at least standard height; or

(b)   a deckhouse of equal height and equivalent strength.

P88 **(2)**   Machinery casings may, however, be exposed if there are no openings giving direct access from the freeboard deck to the machinery space. A door complying with the requirements of regulation 12 is acceptable in the machinery casing, provided that it leads to a space or passageway which is as strongly constructed as the casing and is separated from the stairway to the engine-room by a second weathertight door of steel or other equivalent material.

Gangway and access

P88 **(3)**   A fore-and-aft permanent gangway, constructed in accordance with the provisions of regulation 25-1(2)(e), shall be fitted on type 'A' ships at the level of the superstructure deck between the poop and the midship bridge or deckhouse where fitted. The arrangement contained in regulation 25-1(2)(a) is considered an equivalent means of access to carry out the purpose of the gangway.

P88 **(4)**   Safe access from the gangway level shall be available between separate crew accommodations and also between crew accommodations and the machinery space.

Hatchways

P88 **(5)**   Exposed hatchways on the freeboard and forecastle decks or on the tops of expansion trunks on type 'A' ships shall be provided with efficient watertight covers of steel or other equivalent material.

Freeing arrangements

P88 **(6)**   Type 'A' ships with bulwarks shall have open rails fitted for at least half the length of the weather deck or other equivalent freeing arrangements. A freeing port area, in the lower part of the bulwarks, of 33% of the total area of the bulwarks, is an acceptable equivalent freeing arrangement. The upper edge of the sheer strake shall be kept as low as practicable.

P88 **(7)**   Where superstructures are connected by trunks, open rails shall be fitted for the whole length of the exposed parts of the freeboard deck.

Chapter III
Freeboards

Regulation 27
Types of ships

P88 **(1)** For the purposes of freeboard computation, ships shall be divided into type 'A' and type 'B'.

Type 'A' ships

P88 **(2)** A type 'A' ship is a ship which:

(a) is designed to carry only liquid cargoes in bulk;

(b) has a high integrity of the exposed deck with only small access openings to cargo compartments, closed by watertight gasketed covers of steel or equivalent material; and

(c) has low permeability of loaded cargo compartments.

P88 **(3)** A type 'A' ship, if over 150 m in length, to which a freeboard less than type 'B' has been assigned, when loaded in accordance with the requirements of paragraph (11), shall be able to withstand the flooding of any compartment or compartments, with an assumed permeability of 0.95, consequent upon the damage assumptions specified in paragraph (12), and shall remain afloat in a satisfactory condition of equilibrium, as specified in paragraph (13). In such a ship, the machinery space shall be treated as a floodable compartment, but with a permeability of 0.85.

P88 **(4)** A type 'A' ship shall be assigned a freeboard not less than that given in table 28.1.

Type 'B' ships

P88 **(5)** All ships which do not come within the provisions regarding type 'A' ships in paragraphs (2) and (3) shall be considered as type 'B' ships.

P88 **(6)** Type 'B' ships, which in position 1 have hatch covers which are permitted by the Administration to comply with the requirements of regulation 15 (other than paragraph (6)) or which are fitted with securing arrangements accepted under the provisions of regulation 16(6), shall be assigned freeboards based upon the values given in table 28.2, increased by the values given in table 27.1:

Table 27.1 – *Freeboard increase over tabular freeboard for type 'B' ships, for ships with hatch covers not complying with regulation 15 (other than paragraph 6)*

Length of ship (m)	Freeboard increase (mm)	Length of ship (m)	Freeboard increase (mm)	Length of ship (m)	Freeboard increase (mm)
108 and below	50	111	57	115	68
		112	59	116	70
109	52	113	62	117	73
110	55	114	64	118	76

Length of ship (m)	Freeboard increase (mm)	Length of ship (m)	Freeboard increase (mm)	Length of ship (m)	Freeboard increase (mm)
119	80	147	215	175	301
120	84	148	219	176	304
121	87	149	224	177	306
122	91	150	228	178	308
123	95	151	232	179	311
124	99	152	236	180	313
125	103	153	240	181	315
126	108	154	244	182	318
127	112	155	247	183	320
128	116	156	251	184	322
129	121	157	254	185	325
130	126	158	258	186	327
131	131	159	261	187	329
132	136	160	264	188	332
133	142	161	267	189	334
134	147	162	270	190	336
135	153	163	273	191	339
136	159	164	275	192	341
137	164	165	278	193	343
138	170	166	280	194	346
139	175	167	283	195	348
140	181	168	285	196	350
141	186	169	287	197	353
142	191	170	290	198	355
143	196	171	292	199	357
144	201	172	294	200	358
145	206	173	297		
146	210	174	299		

Freeboards at intermediate lengths of ship shall be obtained by linear interpolation. Ships above 200 m in length shall be dealt with by the Administration.

P88 **(7)** Type 'B' ships, which in position 1 have hatchways fitted with hatch covers complying with the requirements of regulation 16(2) through (5), shall, except as provided in paragraphs (8) to (13) inclusive, be assigned freeboards based on table 28.2.

P88 **(8)** Any type 'B' ship of over 100 m in length may be assigned freeboards less than those required under paragraph (7), provided that, in relation to the amount of reduction granted, the Administration is satisfied that:

(a) the measures provided for the protection of the crew are adequate;

(b) the freeing arrangements are adequate;

(c) the covers in position 1 and 2 comply with the provisions of regulation 16(1) through (5) and (7); and

(d) the ship, when loaded in accordance with the requirements of paragraph (11), shall be able to withstand the flooding of any

145

compartment or compartments, with an assumed permeability of 0.95, consequent upon the damage assumptions specified in paragraph (12), and shall remain afloat in a satisfactory condition of equilibrium, as specified in paragraph (13). In such a ship, if over 150 m in length, the machinery space shall be treated as a floodable compartment, but with a permeability of 0.85.

Refer to the unified interpretation for regulation 27(7) of the 1966 Convention

---

P88 **(9)**   In calculating the freeboards for type 'B' ships which comply with the requirements of paragraphs (8), (11), (12) and (13), the values from table 28.2 shall not be reduced by more than 60% of the difference between the tabular values in tables 28.1 and 28.2 for the appropriate ship lengths.

P88 **(10)   (a)** The reduction in tabular freeboard allowed under paragraph (9) may be increased up to the total difference between the values in table 28.1 and those in table 28.2 on condition that the ship complies with the requirements of:

(i)   regulation 26, other than paragraph (5), as if it were a type 'A' ship;

(ii)   paragraphs (8), (11) and (13); and

(iii)   paragraph (12), provided that throughout the length of the ship any one transverse bulkhead will be assumed to be damaged, such that two adjacent fore and aft compartments shall be flooded simultaneously, except that such damage will not apply to the boundary bulkheads of a machinery space.

P88   **(b)** In such a ship, if over 150 m in length, the machinery space shall be treated as a floodable compartment, but with a permeability of 0.85.

Initial condition of loading

P88 **(11)**   The initial condition of loading before flooding shall be determined as follows:

(a)   The ship is loaded to its Summer Load Line on an imaginary even keel.

(b)   When calculating the vertical centre of gravity, the following principles apply:

(i)   homogeneous cargo is carried.

(ii)   all cargo compartments, except those referred to under subparagraph (iii), but including compartments intended to be partially filled, shall be considered fully loaded except that in the case of fluid cargoes each compartment shall be treated as 98% full.

(iii)   if the ship is intended to operate at its Summer Load Line with empty compartments, such compartments shall be considered empty, provided the height of the centre of gravity so calculated is not less than as calculated under subparagraph (ii);

(iv) 50% of the individual total capacity of all tanks and spaces fitted to contain consumable liquids and stores is allowed for. It shall be assumed that for each type of liquid at least one transverse pair or a single centreline tank has maximum free surface, and the tank or combination of tanks to be taken into account shall be those where the effect of free surfaces is the greatest; in each tank the centre of gravity of the contents shall be taken at the centre of volume of the tank. The remaining tanks shall be assumed either completely empty or completely filled, and the distribution of consumable liquids between these tanks shall be effected so as to obtain the greatest possible height above the keel for the centre of gravity;

(v) at an angle of heel of not more than 5° in each compartment containing liquids, as prescribed in subparagraph (ii), except that in the case of compartments containing consumable fluids, as prescribed in subparagraph (iv), the maximum free surface effect shall be taken into account. Alternatively, the actual free surface effects may be used, provided the methods of calculation are acceptable to the Administration;

(vi) weights shall be calculated on the basis of the following values for specific gravities:

salt water	1.025
fresh water	1.000
oil fuel	0.950
diesel oil	0.900
lubricating oil	0.900

Damage assumptions

P88 **(12)** The following principles regarding the character of the assumed damage apply:

(a) The vertical extent of damage in all cases is assumed to be from the base line upwards without limit.

(b) The transverse extent of damage is equal to $B/5$ or 11.5 m, whichever is the lesser, measured inboard from the side of the ship perpendicularly to the centreline at the level of the Summer Load Line.

(c) If damage of a lesser extent than specified in subparagraphs (a) and (b) results in a more severe condition, such lesser extent shall be assumed.

(d) Except where otherwise required by paragraph (10)(a), the flooding shall be confined to a single compartment between adjacent transverse bulkheads, provided that the inner longitudinal boundary of the compartment is not in a position within the transverse extent of assumed damage. Transverse boundary bulkheads of wing tanks which do not extend over the full breadth of the ship shall be assumed not to be damaged, provided that they extend beyond the transverse extent of assumed damage prescribed in subparagraph (b).

If in a transverse bulkhead there are steps or recesses of not more than 3 m in length, located within the transverse extent of assumed damage as defined in subparagraph (b), such transverse bulkhead may be considered intact and the adjacent compartment may be floodable singly. If, however, within the transverse extent of assumed damage there is a step or recess of more than 3 m in length in a transverse bulkhead, the two compartments adjacent to this bulkhead shall be considered as flooded. The step formed by the afterpeak bulkhead and the afterpeak tank top shall not be regarded as a step for the purpose of this regulation.

(e) Where a main transverse bulkhead is located within the transverse extent of assumed damage and is stepped in way of a double bottom or side tank by more than 3 m, the double bottom or side tanks adjacent to the stepped portion of the main transverse bulkhead shall be considered as flooded simultaneously. If this side tank has openings into one or several holds, such as grain feeding holes, such hold or holds shall be considered as flooded simultaneously. Similarly in a ship designed for the carriage of fluid cargoes, if a side tank has openings into adjacent compartments, such adjacent compartments shall be considered as empty and as being flooded simultaneously. This provision is applicable even where such openings are fitted with closing appliances, except in the case of sluice valves fitted in bulkheads between tanks and where the valves are controlled from the deck. Manhole covers with closely spaced bolts are considered equivalent to the unpierced bulkhead, except in the case of openings in topside tanks making the topside tanks common to the holds.

(f) Where the flooding of any two adjacent fore and aft compartments is envisaged, main transverse watertight bulkheads shall be spaced at least $\frac{1}{3} L^{\frac{2}{3}}$ or 14.5 m, whichever is the lesser, in order to be considered effective. Where transverse bulkheads are spaced at a lesser distance, one or more of these bulkheads shall be assumed as non-existent in order to achieve the minimum spacing between bulkheads.

Condition of equilibrium

(13) The condition of equilibrium after flooding shall be regarded as satisfactory provided:

(a) The final waterline after flooding, taking into account sinkage, heel and trim, is below the lower edge of any opening through which progressive downflooding may take place. Such openings shall include air pipes, ventilators (even if they comply with regulation 19(4)) and openings which are closed by means of weathertight doors (even if they comply with regulation 12) or hatch covers (even if they comply with regulation 16(1) through (5)), and may exclude those openings closed by means of manhole covers and flush scuttles (which comply with regulation 18), cargo hatch covers of the type described in regulation 27(2), remotely operated sliding watertight doors, and sidescuttles of the non-opening type (which comply with regulation 23). However, in the case of doors separating a main machinery space from a steering gear compartment, watertight doors may be of a hinged, quick-acting type kept closed at sea whilst not in use, provided also that the lower sill of such doors is above the Summer Load Line.

(b) If pipes, ducts or tunnels are situated within the assumed extent of damage penetration as defined in paragraph (12)(b), arrangements shall be made so that progressive flooding cannot thereby extend to compartments other than those assumed to be floodable in the calculation for each case of damage.

(c) The angle of heel due to unsymmetrical flooding does not exceed 15°. If no part of the deck is immersed, an angle of heel of up to 17° may be accepted.

(d) The metacentric height in the flooded condition is positive.

(e) When any part of the deck outside the compartment assumed flooded in a particular case of damage is immersed, or in any case where the margin of stability in the flooded condition may be considered doubtful, the residual stability is to be investigated. It may be regarded as sufficient if the righting-lever curve has a minimum range of 20° beyond the position of equilibrium with a maximum righting lever of at least 0.1 m within this range. The area under the righting-lever curve within this range shall be not less than 0.0175 m·rad. The Administration shall give consideration to the potential hazard presented by protected or unprotected openings which may become temporarily immersed within the range of residual stability.

(f) The Administration is satisfied that the stability is sufficient during intermediate stages of flooding.

Ships without means of propulsion

P88 **(14)** A lighter, barge or other ship without independent means of propulsion shall be assigned a freeboard in accordance with the provisions of these regulations. Barges which meet the requirements of paragraphs (2) and (3) may be assigned type 'A' freeboards:

(a) The Administration should especially consider the stability of barges with cargo on the weather deck. Deck cargo can only be carried on barges to which the ordinary type 'B' freeboard is assigned.

(b) However, in the case of barges which are unmanned, the requirements of regulations 25, 26(3), 26(4) and 39 shall not apply.

(c) Such unmanned barges which have on the freeboard deck only small access openings closed by watertight gasketed covers of steel or equivalent material may be assigned a freeboard 25% less than those calculated in accordance with these regulations.

Refer to the unified interpretation for regulation 27(11) of the 1966 Convention *(IACS interpretation LL.42)*

Regulation 28
Freeboard tables

see also the unified interpretation

Type 'A' ships

[P88] **(1)** The tabular freeboard for type 'A' ships shall be determined from table 28.1:

[P88] **Table 28.1** – *Freeboard table for type 'A' ships*

Length of ship (m)	Freeboard (mm)	Length of ship (m)	Freeboard (mm)	Length of ship (m)	Freeboard (mm)
24	200	52	467	80	841
25	208	53	478	81	855
26	217	54	490	82	869
27	225	55	503	83	883
28	233	56	516	84	897
29	242	57	530	85	911
30	250	58	544	86	926
31	258	59	559	87	940
32	267	60	573	88	955
33	275	61	587	89	969
34	283	62	600	90	984
35	292	63	613	91	999
36	300	64	626	92	1014
37	308	65	639	93	1029
38	316	66	653	94	1044
39	325	67	666	95	1059
40	334	68	680	96	1074
41	344	69	693	97	1089
42	354	70	706	98	1105
43	364	71	720	99	1120
44	374	72	733	100	1135
45	385	73	746	101	1151
46	396	74	760	102	1166
47	408	75	773	103	1181
48	420	76	786	104	1196
49	432	77	800	105	1212
50	443	78	814	106	1228
51	455	79	828	107	1244

P88 **Table 28.1** *(continued)*

Length of ship (m)	Freeboard (mm)	Length of ship (m)	Freeboard (mm)	Length of ship (m)	Freeboard (mm)
108	1260	153	2016	198	2592
109	1276	154	2032	199	2602
110	1293	155	2048	200	2612
111	1309	156	2064	201	2622
112	1326	157	2080	202	2632
113	1342	158	2096	203	2641
114	1359	159	2111	204	2650
115	1376	160	2126	205	2659
116	1392	161	2141	206	2669
117	1409	162	2155	207	2678
118	1426	163	2169	208	2687
119	1442	164	2184	209	2696
120	1459	165	2198	210	2705
121	1476	166	2212	211	2714
122	1494	167	2226	212	2723
123	1511	168	2240	213	2732
124	1528	169	2254	214	2741
125	1546	170	2268	215	2749
126	1563	171	2281	216	2758
127	1580	172	2294	217	2767
128	1598	173	2307	218	2775
129	1615	174	2320	219	2784
130	1632	175	2332	220	2792
131	1650	176	2345	221	2801
132	1667	177	2357	222	2809
133	1684	178	2369	223	2817
134	1702	179	2381	224	2825
135	1719	180	2393	225	2833
136	1736	181	2405	226	2841
137	1753	182	2416	227	2849
138	1770	183	2428	228	2857
139	1787	184	2440	229	2865
140	1803	185	2451	230	2872
141	1820	186	2463	231	2880
142	1837	187	2474	232	2888
143	1853	188	2486	233	2895
144	1870	189	2497	234	2903
145	1886	190	2508	235	2910
146	1903	191	2519	236	2918
147	1919	192	2530	237	2925
148	1935	193	2541	238	2932
149	1952	194	2552	239	2939
150	1968	195	2562	240	2946
151	1984	196	2572	241	2953
152	2000	197	2582	242	2959

P88 **Table 28.1** *(continued)*

Length of ship (m)	Freeboard (mm)	Length of ship (m)	Freeboard (mm)	Length of ship (m)	Freeboard (mm)
243	2966	284	3194	325	3345
244	2973	285	3198	326	3347
245	2979	286	3202	327	3350
246	2986	287	3207	328	3353
247	2993	288	3211	329	3355
248	3000	289	3215	330	3358
249	3006	290	3220	331	3361
250	3012	291	3224	332	3363
251	3018	292	3228	333	3366
252	3024	293	3233	334	3368
253	3030	294	3237	335	3371
254	3036	295	3241	336	3373
255	3042	296	3246	337	3375
256	3048	297	3250	338	3378
257	3054	298	3254	339	3380
258	3060	299	3258	340	3382
259	3066	300	3262	341	3385
260	3072	301	3266	342	3387
261	3078	302	3270	343	3389
262	3084	303	3274	344	3392
263	3089	304	3278	345	3394
264	3095	305	3281	346	3396
265	3101	306	3285	347	3399
266	3106	307	3288	348	3401
267	3112	308	3292	349	3403
268	3117	309	3295	350	3406
269	3123	310	3298	351	3408
270	3128	311	3302	352	3410
271	3133	312	3305	353	3412
272	3138	313	3308	354	3414
273	3143	314	3312	355	3416
274	3148	315	3315	356	3418
275	3153	316	3318	357	3420
276	3158	317	3322	358	3422
277	3163	318	3325	359	3423
278	3167	319	3328	360	3425
279	3172	320	3331	361	3427
280	3176	321	3334	362	3428
281	3181	322	3337	363	3430
282	3185	323	3339	364	3432
283	3189	324	3342	365	3433

Freeboards at intermediate lengths of ship shall be obtained by linear interpolation. Ships above 365 m in length shall be dealt with by the Administration.

Type 'B' ships

[P88] **(2)** The tabular freeboard for type 'B' ships shall be determined from table 28.2:

[P88] **Table 28.2** – *Freeboard table for type 'B' ships*

Length of ship (m)	Freeboard (mm)	Length of ship (m)	Freeboard (mm)	Length of ship (m)	Freeboard (mm)
24	200	65	644	106	1401
25	208	66	659	107	1421
26	217	67	674	108	1440
27	225	68	689	109	1459
28	233	69	705	110	1479
29	242	70	721	111	1500
30	250	71	738	112	1521
31	258	72	754	113	1543
32	267	73	769	114	1565
33	275	74	784	115	1587
34	283	75	800	116	1609
35	292	76	816	117	1630
36	300	77	833	118	1651
37	308	78	850	119	1671
38	316	79	868	120	1690
39	325	80	887	121	1709
40	334	81	905	122	1729
41	344	82	923	123	1750
42	354	83	942	124	1771
43	364	84	960	125	1793
44	374	85	978	126	1815
45	385	86	996	127	1837
46	396	87	1015	128	1859
47	408	88	1034	129	1880
48	420	89	1054	130	1901
49	432	90	1075	131	1921
50	443	91	1096	132	1940
51	455	92	1116	133	1959
52	467	93	1135	134	1979
53	478	94	1154	135	2000
54	490	95	1172	136	2021
55	503	96	1190	137	2043
56	516	97	1209	138	2065
57	530	98	1229	139	2087
58	544	99	1250	140	2109
59	559	100	1271	141	2130
60	573	101	1293	142	2151
61	587	102	1315	143	2171
62	601	103	1337	144	2190
63	615	104	1359	145	2209
64	629	105	1380	146	2229

P88 **Table 28.2** *(continued)*

Length of ship (m)	Freeboard (mm)	Length of ship (m)	Freeboard (mm)	Length of ship (m)	Freeboard (mm)
147	2250	192	3134	237	3835
148	2271	193	3151	238	3849
149	2293	194	3167	239	3864
150	2315	195	3185	240	3880
151	2334	196	3202	241	3893
152	2354	197	3219	242	3906
153	2375	198	3235	243	3920
154	2396	199	3249	244	3934
155	2418	200	3264	245	3949
156	2440	201	3280	246	3965
157	2460	202	3296	247	3978
158	2480	203	3313	248	3992
159	2500	204	3330	249	4005
160	2520	205	3347	250	4018
161	2540	206	3363	251	4032
162	2560	207	3380	252	4045
163	2580	208	3397	253	4058
164	2600	209	3413	254	4072
165	2620	210	3430	255	4085
166	2640	211	3445	256	4098
167	2660	212	3460	257	4112
168	2680	213	3475	258	4125
169	2698	214	3490	259	4139
170	2716	215	3505	260	4152
171	2735	216	3520	261	4165
172	2754	217	3537	262	4177
173	2774	218	3554	263	4189
174	2795	219	3570	264	4201
175	2815	220	3586	265	4214
176	2835	221	3601	266	4227
177	2855	222	3615	267	4240
178	2875	223	3630	268	4252
179	2895	224	3645	269	4264
180	2915	225	3660	270	4276
181	2933	226	3675	271	4289
182	2952	227	3690	272	4302
183	2970	228	3705	273	4315
184	2988	229	3720	274	4327
185	3007	230	3735	275	4339
186	3025	231	3750	276	4350
187	3044	232	3765	277	4362
188	3062	233	3780	278	4373
189	3080	234	3795	279	4385
190	3098	235	3808	280	4397
191	3116	236	3821	281	4408

P88 **Table 28.2** *(continued)*

Length of ship (m)	Freeboard (mm)	Length of ship (m)	Freeboard (mm)	Length of Ship (m)	Freeboard (mm)
282	4420	310	4736	338	5035
283	4432	311	4748	339	5045
284	4443	312	4757	340	5055
285	4455	313	4768	341	5065
286	4467	314	4779	342	5075
287	4478	315	4790	343	5086
288	4490	316	4801	344	5097
289	4502	317	4812	345	5108
290	4513	318	4823	346	5119
291	4525	319	4834	347	5130
292	4537	320	4844	348	5140
293	4548	321	4855	349	5150
294	4560	322	4866	350	5160
295	4572	323	4878	351	5170
296	4583	324	4890	352	5180
297	4595	325	4899	353	5190
298	4607	326	4909	354	5200
299	4618	327	4920	355	5210
300	4630	328	4931	356	5220
301	4642	329	4943	357	5230
302	4654	330	4955	358	5240
303	4665	331	4965	359	5250
304	4676	332	4975	360	5260
305	4686	333	4985	361	5268
306	4695	334	4995	362	5276
307	4704	335	5005	363	5285
308	4714	336	5015	364	5294
309	4725	337	5025	365	5303

Freeboards at intermediate lengths of ship shall be obtained by linear interpolation. Ships above 365 m in length shall be dealt with by the Administration.

Regulation 29
Correction to the freeboard for ships under 100 m in length

The tabular freeboard for a type 'B' ship of between 24 m and 100 m in length having enclosed superstructures with an effective length of up to 35% of the length of the ship shall be increased by:

P88 $7.5 \ (100 - L) \ (0.35 - \dfrac{E_1}{L})$ mm

where L is the length of the ship in metres,

E_1 is the effective length E of superstructure in metres as defined in regulation 35, but excluding the length of trunks.

Regulation 30
Correction for block coefficient

Where the block coefficient (C_b) exceeds 0.68, the tabular freeboard specified in regulation 28 as modified, if applicable, by regulations 27(8), 27(10) and 29 shall be multiplied by the factor:

$$\frac{C_b + 0.68}{1.36}$$

[P88] The block coefficient is not to be taken greater than 1.0.

Regulation 31
Correction for depth

(1)   Where D exceeds $\dfrac{L}{15}$ the freeboard shall be increased by $(D - \dfrac{L}{15})R$ mm, where R is $\dfrac{L}{0.48}$ at lengths less than 120 m and 250 at 120 m length and above.

[P88] **(2)**   Where D is less than $\dfrac{L}{15}$ no reduction shall be made, except in a ship with an enclosed superstructure covering at least $0.6L$ amidships, with a complete trunk, or combination of detached enclosed superstructures and trunks which extend all fore and aft, where the freeboard shall be reduced at the rate prescribed in paragraph (1).

[P88] **(3)**   Where the height of the superstructure or trunk is less than the corresponding standard height, the calculated reduction shall be corrected in the ratio of the height of the actual superstructure or trunk to the applicable standard height, as defined in regulation 33.

Regulation 32
Correction for position of deck line

Where the actual depth to the upper edge of the deck line is greater or less than D, the difference between the depths shall be added to or deducted from the freeboard.

[P88] Regulation 32-1
[P88] *Correction for recess in freeboard deck*

[P88] **(1)**   Where a recess is arranged in the freeboard deck, and it does not extend to the sides of the ship, the freeboard calculated without regard to the recess shall be corrected for the consequent loss of buoyancy. The correction shall be equal to the value obtained by dividing the volume of the recess by the waterplane area of the ship at 85% of the least moulded depth (see figure 32-1.1).

[P88] **(2)**   The correction shall be an addition to the freeboard obtained after all other corrections have been applied, except bow height correction.

P88 **(3)** Where the freeboard, corrected for lost buoyancy as above, is greater than the minimum geometric freeboard determined on the basis of a moulded depth measured to the bottom of the recess, the latter value may be used.

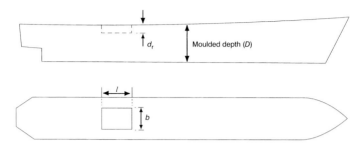

Figure 32-1.1

Correction is the addition to freeboard equal to:

$$\frac{l \times b \times d_r}{\text{WP Area at } 0.85D}$$

Regulation 33
Standard height of superstructure

P88 The standard height of a superstructure shall be as given in table 33.1:

P88 **Table 33.1**

L (m)	Standard height (m)	
	Raised quarterdeck	All other superstructures
30 or less	0.9	1.8
75	1.2	1.8
125 or more	1.8	2.3

The standard heights at intermediate lengths of the ship shall be obtained by linear interpolation.

Regulation 34
Length of superstructure

P88 **(1)** Except as provided in paragraph (2), the length of a superstructure (*S*) shall be the mean length of the parts of the superstructure which lie within the length (*L*).

P88 Where a superstructure bulkhead is recessed, the effective length of the superstructure shall be reduced by an amount equal to the area of the recess in plan view divided by the breadth of the superstructure at the midlength of the

157

recess. Where the recess is unsymmetrical about the centreline, the largest portion of the recess shall be considered as applying to both sides of the ship. A recess need not be decked over.

(2) Where the end bulkhead of an enclosed superstructure extends in a fair convex curve beyond its intersection with the superstructure sides, the length of the superstructure may be increased on the basis of an equivalent plane bulkhead. This increase shall be two-thirds of the fore and aft extent of the curvature. The maximum curvature which may be taken into account in determining this increase is one-half the breadth of the superstructure at the point of intersection of the curved end of the superstructure with its side.

|P88| Where there is an extension to a superstructure, which extension has a breadth on each side of the centreline at least 30% of the breadth of the ship, the effective length of the superstructure may be increased by considering an equivalent superstructure bulkhead in the form of a parabola. This parabola shall extend from the extension at the centreline and pass through the junction of the actual superstructure bulkhead with the sides of the extension and extend to the sides of the ship. This parabola shall be completely contained within the boundary of the superstructure and its extensions.

|P88| If the superstructure is set in from the side, up to the limit allowed under regulation 3(10), the equivalent bulkhead should be calculated on the basis of the actual breadth of the superstructure (and not the breadth of the ship).

|P88| **(3)** Superstructures which have sloped end bulkheads shall be dealt with in the following manner:

> **(a)** When the height of superstructure, clear of the slope, is equal to or smaller than the standard height, the length S is to be obtained as shown in figure 34.1.
>
> **(b)** When the height is greater than the standard, the length S is to be obtained as shown in figure 34.2.
>
> **(c)** The foregoing will apply only when the slope, related to the baseline, is 15° or greater. Where the slope is less than 15°, the configuration shall be treated as sheer.

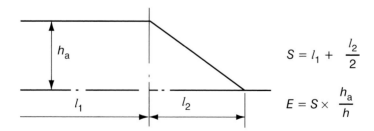

$$S = l_1 + \frac{l_2}{2}$$

$$E = S \times \frac{h_a}{h}$$

Figure 34.1 – *Height of superstructure equal to or smaller than the standard height* h

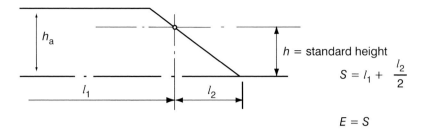

Figure 34.2 – *Height of superstructure greater than the standard height*

Regulation 35
Effective length of superstructure

P88 **(1)**   Except as provided for in paragraph (2), the effective length (*E*) of an enclosed superstructure of standard height shall be its length.

(2)   In all cases where an enclosed superstructure of standard height is set in from the sides of the ship as permitted in regulation 3(10), the effective length shall be the length modified by the ratio of b/B_s, where:

   b is the breadth of the superstructure at the middle of its length; and

   B_s is the breadth of the ship at the middle of the length of the superstructure.

Where a superstructure is set in for a part of its length, this modification shall be applied only to the set-in part.

P88 **(3)**   Where the height of an enclosed superstructure is less than the standard height, the effective length shall be its length reduced in the ratio of the actual height to the standard height. Where the height exceeds the standard, no increase shall be made to the effective length of the superstructure (see figures 34.1 and 34.2).

P88 Where the height, clear of the slope, of a superstructure which has sloped end bulkheads is less than the standard height, its effective length *E* shall be its length *S* as obtained from figure 34.1, reduced in the ratio of the actual height to the standard height.

P88 Where a poop or forecastle of less than standard height is fitted on a ship with excessive sheer but without any superstructure within 0.2*L* amidships, credit may be given to the height of the poop or forecastle by increasing the actual height by the difference between the actual and the standard sheer profiles. The deduction for excess sheer in accordance with regulation 38(16) is not to be granted.

------
see also the unified interpretation
------

(4)   The effective length of a raised quarterdeck, if fitted with an intact front bulkhead, shall be its length up to a maximum of 0.6*L*. Where the bulkhead is not intact, the raised quarterdeck shall be treated as a poop of less than standard height.

P88 The maximum effective length of 0.6L of a raised quarterdeck is to be measured from the after perpendicular, even where a poop is fitted in conjunction with the raised quarterdeck.

see also the unified interpretation of regulation 35(3) and (4)

(5)   Superstructures which are not enclosed shall have no effective length.

Regulation 36
Trunks

(1)   A trunk or similar structure which does not extend to the sides of the ship shall be regarded as efficient on the following conditions:

  (a)   the trunk is at least as strong as a superstructure;

  P88 **(b)**   the hatchways are in the trunk deck, the hatchway coamings and covers comply with the requirements of regulations 13 to 16 inclusive and the width of the trunk deck stringer provides a satisfactory gangway and sufficient lateral stiffness. However, small access openings with watertight covers may be permitted in the freeboard deck;

  (c)   a permanent working platform fore and aft fitted with guard rails is provided by the trunk deck, or by detached trunks connected to superstructures by efficient permanent gangways;

  (d)   ventilators are protected by the trunk, by watertight covers or by other equivalent means;

  P88 **(e)**   open rails are fitted on the weather parts of the freeboard deck in way of the trunk for at least half their length or, alternatively, freeing port area in the lower part of the bulwarks, subject to regulation 24(2), of 33% of the total area of the bulwarks is provided;

  (f)   the machinery casings are protected by the trunk, by a super-structure of at least standard height, or by a deckhouse of the same height and of equivalent strength;

  (g)   the breadth of the trunk is at least 60% of the breadth of the ship; and

  (h)   where there is no superstructure, the length of the trunk is at least 0.6L.

(2)   The full length of an efficient trunk reduced in the ratio of its mean breadth to B shall be its effective length.

(3)   The standard height of a trunk is the standard height of a superstructure other than a raised quarterdeck.

P88 **(4)**   Where the height of a trunk is less than the standard height, its effective length shall be reduced in the ratio of the actual to the standard height. Where the height of hatchway coamings on the trunk deck is less than that required under regulation 14-1, a reduction from the actual height of trunk shall be made which corresponds to the difference between the actual and the required height of coaming.

P88 **(5)** Where the trunk height is less than standard and the trunk hatch coamings are also of less than standard height, or omitted entirely, the reduction from the actual height of trunk on account of insufficient hatch coaming height shall be taken as the difference between 600 mm and the actual height of coaming, or 600 mm if no hatch coamings are fitted. Reduction in the actual height of trunk shall not be required in cases where only small hatches with less than standard height are fitted in the trunk deck for which dispensation from the requirement of standard coaming height may be given.

P88 **(6)** Continuous hatchways may be treated as a trunk in the freeboard computation, provided the provisions of this paragraph are complied with in all respects.

P88 The trunk deck stringer referred to in paragraph (1)(b) may be fitted outboard of the trunk side bulkhead in association with the following:

(a) the stringer so formed is to provide a clear walkway of at least 450 mm in width on each side of the ship;

(b) the stringer is to be of solid plate, efficiently supported and stiffened;

(c) the stringer is to be as high above the freeboard deck as practicable. In the freeboard calculation, the trunk height is to be reduced by at least 600 mm or by the actual difference between the top of the trunk and the stringer, whichever is greater;

(d) hatch cover securing appliances are to be accessible from the stringer or walkway; and

(e) the breadth of the trunk is to be measured between the trunk side bulkheads.

P88 **(7)** Where the trunk adjoining the superstructures such as poop, bridge or forecastle is included in the calculation of freeboard, openings shall not be arranged in that part of the bulkhead which is common for the trunk and superstructure. A relaxation may be made for small openings such as for piping, cable or manholes with covers attached by means of bolts.

P88 **(8)** The sides of a trunk included in the calculation of freeboard shall be intact. Sidescuttles of the non–opening type and bolted manhole covers may be allowed.

Regulation 37
Deduction for superstructures and trunks

P88 **(1)** Where the effective length of superstructures and trunks is $1L$, the deduction from the freeboard shall be 350 mm at 24 m length of ship, 860 mm at 85 m length, and 1070 mm at 122 m length and above; deductions at intermediate lengths shall be obtained by linear interpolation.

P88 **(2)** Where the total effective length of superstructures and trunks is less than $1L$, the deduction shall be a percentage obtained from table 37.1:

[P88] **Table 37.1** – *Percentage of deduction
for type 'A' and 'B' ships*

	Total effective length of superstructures and trunks										
0	**0.1L**	**0.2L**	**0.3L**	**0.4L**	**0.5L**	**0.6L**	**0.7L**	**0.8L**	**0.9L**	**1L**
Percentage of deduction for all types of superstructure	0	7	14	21	31	41	52	63	75.3	87.7	100

[P88] Percentages at intermediate lengths of superstructures and trunks shall be obtained by linear interpolation.

[P88] **(3)**   For ships of type 'B' where the effective length of a forecastle is less than 0.07L, no deduction is allowed.

Regulation 38
Sheer

General

(1)   The sheer shall be measured from the deck at side to a line of reference drawn parallel to the keel through the sheer line amidships.

(2)   In ships designed with a rake of keel, the sheer shall be measured in relation to a reference line drawn parallel to the design load waterline.

(3)   In flush deck ships and in ships with detached superstructures the sheer shall be measured at the freeboard deck.

(4)   In ships with topsides of unusual form in which there is a step or break in the topsides, the sheer shall be considered in relation to the equivalent depth amidships.

[P88] **(5)**   In ships with a superstructure of standard height which extends over the whole length of the freeboard deck, the sheer shall be measured at the superstructure deck. Where the height exceeds the standard, the least difference (Z) between the actual and standard heights shall be added to each end ordinate. Similarly, the intermediate ordinates at distances of $\frac{1}{6}L$ and $\frac{1}{3}L$ from each perpendicular shall be increased by $0.444Z$ and $0.111Z$ respectively. Where there is an enclosed poop or forecastle superimposed on the superstructure, sheer credit shall be allowed for such a poop or forecastle, according to the method of paragraph (12) as shown in figure 38.1.

(6)   Where the deck of an enclosed superstructure has at least the same sheer as the exposed freeboard deck, the sheer of the enclosed portion of the freeboard deck shall not be taken into account.

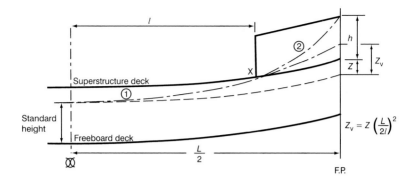

[P88] **Figure 38.1**

[P88] **(7)** Where an enclosed poop or forecastle is of standard height with greater sheer than that of the freeboard deck, or is of more than standard height, an addition to the sheer of the freeboard deck shall be made as provided in paragraph (12).

[P88] Where a poop or forecastle consists of two layers, the method shown in figure 38.2 shall be used.

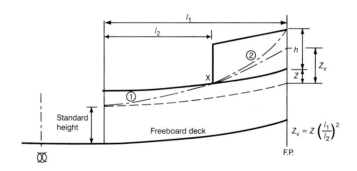

[P88] **Figure 38.2**

[P88] In figures 38.1 and 38.2, the following definitions apply:

Z is as defined in paragraph (5); and

Z_v is the end ordinate of a virtual standard parabolic curve taken through the point "X". If Z_v is greater than $(Z + h)$, the end ordinate shall be $(Z + h)$, in which case point "X" shall be disregarded and curve ② not taken into account.

[P88] When the length of the first tier superstructure is greater than $0.5l$, the virtual standard parabolic curve shall commence at amidships as indicated in figure 38.1.

Standard sheer profile

[P88] **(8)** The ordinates of the standard sheer profile are given in table 38.1:

163

[P88] **Table 38.1** – *Standard sheer profile*
(where L is in metres)

	Station	Ordinate (in mm)	Factor
After half	After perpendicular	$25(\frac{L}{3} + 10)$	1
	$\frac{1}{6} L$ from A.P.	$11.1(\frac{L}{3} + 10)$	3
	$\frac{1}{3} L$ from A.P.	$2.8(\frac{L}{3} + 10)$	3
	Amidships	0	1
Forward half	Amidships	0	1
	$\frac{1}{3} L$ from F.P.	$5.6(\frac{L}{3} + 10)$	3
	$\frac{1}{6} L$ from F.P.	$22.2(\frac{L}{3} + 10)$	3
	Forward perpendicular	$50(\frac{L}{3} + 10)$	1

Measurement of variation from standard sheer profile

[P88] **(9)** Where the sheer profile differs from the standard, the four ordinates of each profile in the forward or after half shall be multiplied by the appropriate factors given in the above table of ordinates. The difference between the sums of the respective products and those of the standard divided by 8 measures the deficiency or excess of sheer in the forward or after half. The arithmetical mean of the excess or deficiency in the forward and after halves measures the excess or deficiency of sheer.

(10) Where the after half of the sheer profile is greater than the standard and the forward half is less than the standard, no credit shall be allowed for the part in excess and deficiency only shall be measured.

[P88] **(11)** Where the forward half of the sheer profile exceeds the standard, and the after portion of the sheer profile is not less than 75% of the standard, credit shall be allowed for the part in excess. Where the after part is less than 50% of the standard, no credit shall be given for the excess sheer forward. Where the after sheer is between 50% and 75% of the standard, intermediate allowances may be granted for excess sheer forward.

[P88] **(12)** Where sheer credit is given for a poop or forecastle the following formula shall be used:

$$s = \frac{yL'}{3L}$$

where s is the sheer credit, to be deducted from the deficiency, or added to the excess of sheer,

y is the difference between actual and standard height of super-structure at the after or forward perpendicular,

L' is the mean enclosed length of poop or forecastle up to a maximum length of $0.5L$, and

L is the length of the ship as defined in regulation 3(1).

The above formula provides a curve in the form of a parabola tangent to the actual sheer curve at the freeboard deck and intersecting the end ordinate at a point below the superstructure deck a distance equal to the standard height of a superstructure. The superstructure deck shall not be less than standard height above this curve at any point. This curve shall be used in determining the sheer profile for forward and after halves of the ship.

P88 **(13)**   **(a)**   Any excess in the height of a superstructure which does not extend to the after perpendicular cannot be regarded as contributing to the sheer allowance.

(b)   Where the height of a superstructure is less than standard, the superstructure deck shall not be less than the minimum height of the superstructure above the virtual sheer curve at any point. For this purpose y shall be taken as the difference between the actual and minimum height of the superstructure at the after/forward perpendicular.

(c)   For a raised quarterdeck credit may be given only when the height of this quarterdeck is greater than the standard height of 'other super-structures' as defined in regulation 33, and only for the amount by which the actual height of the raised quarterdeck exceeds that standard height.

(d)   When a poop or a forecastle has sloping end bulkheads, the sheer credit may be allowed on account of excess height. The formula given in paragraph (12) shall be used, the values for y and L' being as shown in figure 38.3.

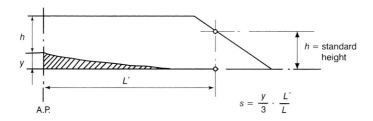

P88 **Figure 38.3** – *Sheer credit s for excess height*

Correction for variations from standard sheer profile

P88 **(14)**   The correction for sheer shall be the deficiency or excess of sheer (see paragraphs (9) to (11) inclusive), multiplied by

$$0.75 - \frac{S_1}{2L}$$

where S_1 is the total length S of enclosed superstructures as defined in regulation 34 without trunks.

Addition for deficiency in sheer

[P88] **(15)**   Where the sheer is less than the standard, the correction for deficiency in sheer (see paragraph (14)) shall be added to the freeboard.

Deduction for excess sheer

[P88] **(16)**   In ships where an enclosed superstructure covers 0.1L before and 0.1L abaft amidships, the correction for excess of sheer as calculated under the provisions of paragraph (14) shall be deducted from the freeboard; in ships where no enclosed superstructure covers amidships, no deduction shall be made from the freeboard; where an enclosed superstructure covers less than 0.1L before and 0.1L abaft amidships, the deduction shall be obtained by linear interpolation. The maximum deduction for excess sheer shall be at the rate of 125 mm per 100 m of length.

[P88] In applying this paragraph, the height of the superstructure shall be related to its standard height. Where the height of the superstructure or raised quarterdeck is less than standard, the reduction shall be in the ratio of the actual to the standard height thereof.

Regulation 39
[P88] *Minimum bow height and reserve buoyancy*

[P88] **(1)**   The bow height (F_b), defined as the vertical distance at the forward perpendicular between the waterline corresponding to the assigned summer freeboard and the designed trim and the top of the exposed deck at side, shall be not less than:

$$F_b = (6075(\tfrac{L}{100}) - 1875(\tfrac{L}{100})^2 + 200(\tfrac{L}{100})^3) \times (2.08 + 0.609C_b - 1.603C_{wf} - 0.0129(\tfrac{L}{d_1}))$$

where:

F_b is the calculated minimum bow height, in millimetres;

L is the length, as defined in regulation 3, in metres;

B is the moulded breadth, as defined in regulation 3, in metres;

d_1 is the draught at 85% of the depth D, in metres;

C_b is the block coefficient, as defined in regulation 3;

C_{wf} is the waterplane area coefficient forward of $\frac{L}{2}$: $C_{wf} = \frac{A_{wf}}{(\frac{L}{2}) \times B}$;

A_{wf} is the waterplane area forward of $\frac{L}{2}$ at draught d_1, in square metres.

[P88] For ships to which timber freeboards are assigned, the summer freeboard (and not the timber summer freeboard) is to be assumed when applying paragraph (1).

[P88] **(2)**   Where the bow height required in paragraph (1) is obtained by sheer, the sheer shall extend for at least 15% of the length of the ship measured from the forward perpendicular. Where it is obtained by fitting a superstructure, such superstructure shall extend from the stem to a point at least 0.07L abaft the forward perpendicular, and shall be enclosed as defined in regulation 3(10).

(3) Ships which, to suit exceptional operational requirements, cannot meet the requirements of paragraphs (1) and (2) of this regulation may be given special consideration by the Administration.

P88 **(4)** **(a)** The sheer of the forecastle deck may be taken into account, even if the length of the forecastle is less than $0.15L$, but greater than $0.07L$, provided that the forecastle height is not less than one half of the standard height of superstructure as defined in regulation 33 between $0.07L$ and the forward perpendicular.

P88 **(b)** Where the forecastle height is less than one half of the standard height of superstructure, as defined in regulation 33, the credited bow height may be determined as follows:

    (i) Where the freeboard deck has sheer extending from abaft $0.15L$, by a parabolic curve having its origin at $0.15L$ abaft the forward perpendicular at a height equal to the midship depth of the ship, extended through the point of intersection of forecastle bulkhead and deck, and up to a point at the forward perpendicular not higher than the level of the forecastle deck (as illustrated in figure 39.1). However, if the value of the height denoted h_t in figure 39.1 is smaller than the value of the height denoted h_b then h_t may be replaced by h_b in the available bow height.

    (ii) Where the freeboard deck has sheer extending for less than $0.15L$ or has no sheer, by a line from the forecastle deck at side at $0.07L$ extended parallel to the baseline to the forward perpendicular (as illustrated in figure 39.2).

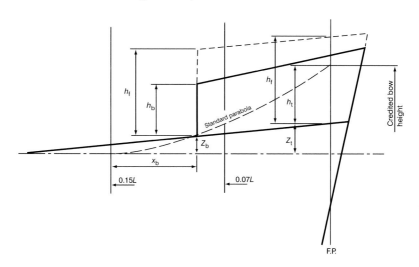

P88 **Figure 39.1**

$$P88 \quad h_t = Z_b \frac{(0.15L)^2}{X_b} - Z_t$$

167

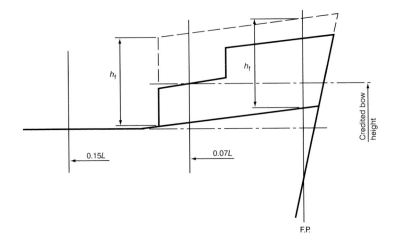

P88 **Figure 39.2**

h_f = Half standard height of superstructure as defined in regulation 33.

P88 **(5)** All ships assigned a type 'B' freeboard, other than oil tankers[*], chemical tankers[*] and gas carriers[*], shall have additional reserve buoyancy in the fore end. Within the range of 0.15L abaft of the forward perpendicular, the sum of the projected area between the Summer Load Line and the deck at side (A1 and A2 in figure 39.3) and the projected area of an enclosed superstructure, if fitted, (A3) shall not be less than:

$$(0.15F_{min} + 4(\tfrac{L}{3} + 10))\tfrac{L}{1000} \ (m^2),$$

where: F_{min} is calculated by: $F_{min} = (F_0 \times f_1) + f_2$;

F_0 is the tabular freeboard, in millimetres, taken from table 28.2, corrected for regulation 27(9) or 27(10), as applicable;

f_1 is the correction for block coefficient given in regulation 30; and

f_2 is the correction for depth, in millimetres, given in regulation 31.

---

[*] Oil tankers, chemical tankers and gas carriers are defined in the International Convention for the Safety of Life at Sea, in force, regulations II-1/2.12, VII/8.2 and VII/11.2, respectively.

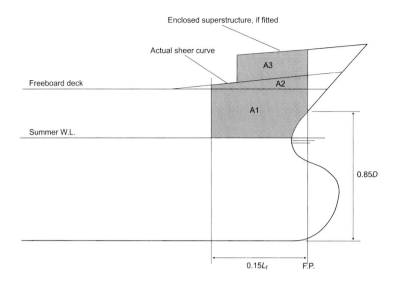

Enclosed superstructure, if fitted

Actual sheer curve

A3

A2

Freeboard deck

A1

Summer W.L.

0.85D

0.15L_f F.P.

P88 **Figure 39.3**

Regulation 40
Minimum freeboards

see also the unified interpretation

Summer freeboard

(1)   The minimum freeboard in summer shall be the freeboard derived from the tables in regulation 28, as modified by the corrections in regulations 27, as applicable, 29, 30, 31, 32, 37, 38 and, if applicable, 39.

P88 **(2)**   The freeboard in salt water, as calculated in accordance with paragraph (1), but without the correction for deck line, as provided by regulation 32, shall not be less than 50 mm. For ships having in position 1 hatchways with covers which do not comply with the requirements of regulation 16(1) through (5) or regulation 26, the freeboard shall be not less than 150 mm.

Tropical freeboard

(3)   The minimum freeboard in the Tropical Zone shall be the freeboard obtained by a deduction from the summer freeboard of one forty-eighth of the summer draught measured from the top of the keel to the centre of the ring of the load line mark.

P88 **(4)**   The freeboard in salt water, as calculated in accordance with paragraph (3), but without the correction for deck line, as provided by regulation 32, shall not be less than 50 mm. For ships having in position 1 hatchways with covers which do not comply with the requirements of regulation 16(1) through (5) or regulation 26, the freeboard shall be not less than 150 mm.

169

Winter freeboard

(5) The minimum freeboard in winter shall be the freeboard obtained by an addition to the summer freeboard of one forty-eighth of summer draught, measured from the top of the keel to the centre of the ring of the load line mark.

Winter North Atlantic freeboard

P88 **(6)** The minimum freeboard for ships of not more than 100 m in length which enter any part of the North Atlantic defined in regulation 52 (annex II) during the winter seasonal period shall be the winter freeboard plus 50 mm. For other ships, the winter North Atlantic freeboard shall be the winter freeboard.

Fresh water freeboard

P88 **(7)** The minimum freeboard in fresh water of unit density shall be obtained by deducting from the minimum freeboard in salt water:

$$\frac{\Delta}{40T} \text{ cm}$$

where Δ is the displacement in salt water in tonnes at the Summer Load Line

T is the tonnes per centimetre immersion in salt water at the Summer Load Line.

P88 **(8)** Where the displacement at the Summer Load Line cannot be certified, the deduction shall be one forty-eighth of summer draught, measured from the top of the keel to the centre of the ring of the load line mark.

Chapter IV
Special requirements for ships assigned timber freeboards

Regulation 41
Application of this chapter

Regulations 42 to 45 inclusive apply only to ships to which timber load lines are assigned.

Regulation 42
Definitions

P88 **(1)** *Timber deck cargo.* The term "timber deck cargo" means a cargo of timber carried on an uncovered part of a freeboard deck. The term does not include wood pulp or similar cargo.*

(2) *Timber load line.* A timber deck cargo may be regarded as giving a ship a certain additional buoyancy and a greater degree of protection against the sea. For that reason, ships carrying a timber deck cargo may be granted a reduction of freeboard calculated according to the provisions of regulation 45 and marked on the ship's side in accordance with the provisions of regulations 6(3) and (4). However, in order that such special freeboard may be granted and used, the timber deck cargo shall comply with certain conditions which are laid down in regulation 44, and the ship itself shall also comply with certain conditions relating to its construction which are set out in regulation 43.

Regulation 43
P88 *Construction of the ship*

Superstructure

P88 **(1)** Ships shall have a forecastle of at least standard height and a length of at least 0.07L. In addition, if the ship is less than 100 m in length, a poop of at least standard height or a raised quarterdeck with a deckhouse of at least the same total height shall be fitted aft.

Double bottom tanks

P88 **(2)** Double bottom tanks, where fitted within the midship half length of the ship, shall have adequate watertight longitudinal subdivision.

Bulwarks

(3) The ship shall be fitted either with permanent bulwarks at least 1 m in height, specially stiffened on the upper edge and supported by strong bulwark stays attached to the deck and provided with necessary freeing ports, or with efficient rails of the same height and of specially strong construction.

---

* Refer to the Code of Safe Practice for Ships carrying Timber Deck Cargoes, adopted by the Organization by resolution A.715(17), as amended.

Regulation 44
Stowage

General

P88 **(1)**   Openings in the deck exposed to weather over which cargo is stowed shall be securely closed and battened down.

The ventilators and air pipes shall be efficiently protected.

P88 **(2)**   Timber deck cargoes shall extend over at least the entire available length which is the total length of the well or wells between superstructures.

Where there is no limiting superstructure at the after end, the timber shall extend at least to the after end of the aftermost hatchway.

P88 The timber deck cargo shall extend athwartships as close as possible to the ship's side, due allowance being made for obstructions such as guard rails, bulwark stays, uprights, pilot access, etc., provided that any gap thus created at the side of the ship shall not exceed a mean of 4% of the breadth. The timber shall be stowed as solidly as possible to at least the standard height of the superstructure other than any raised quarterdeck.

P88 **(3)**   On a ship within a seasonal winter zone in winter, the height of the deck cargo above the deck exposed to weather shall not exceed one third of the extreme breadth of the ship.

P88 **(4)**   The timber deck cargo shall be compactly stowed, lashed and secured. It shall not interfere in any way with the navigation and necessary work of the ship.

Uprights

P88 **(5)**   Uprights, when required by the nature of the timber, shall be of adequate strength considering the breadth of the ship; the strength of the uprights shall not exceed the strength of the bulwark and the spacing shall be suitable for the length and character of timber carried, but shall not exceed 3 m. Strong angles or metal sockets or equally efficient means shall be provided for securing the uprights.

Lashings

P88 **(6)**   Timber deck cargo shall be effectively secured throughout its length by a lashing system acceptable to the Administration for the character of the timber carried.[*]

Stability

P88 **(7)**   Provision shall be made for a safe margin of stability at all stages of the voyage, regard being given to additions of weight, such as those arising from absorption of water or icing, if applicable, and to losses of weight such as those arising from consumption of fuel and stores.

---

[*] Reference is made to the Code of Safe Practice for Ships carrying Timber Deck Cargoes, adopted by the Organization by resolution A.715(17), as amended.

Protection of crew, access to machinery spaces, etc.

[P88] **(8)** In addition to the requirements of regulation 25(5), guard rails or lifelines not more than 350 mm apart vertically shall be provided on each side of the cargo deck to a height of at least 1 m above the cargo.

In addition a lifeline, preferably wire rope set up taut with a stretching screw, shall be provided as near as practicable to the centreline of the ship. The stanchion supports to all guard rails and lifelines shall be so spaced as to prevent undue sagging. Where the cargo is uneven, a safe walking surface of not less than 600 mm in width shall be fitted over the cargo and effectively secured beneath or adjacent to the lifeline.

[P88] **(9)** Where the requirements prescribed in paragraph (8) are impracticable, alternative arrangements satisfactory to the Administration shall be used.

Steering arrangements

[P88] **(10)** Steering arrangements shall be effectively protected from damage by cargo and, as far as practicable, shall be accessible. Efficient provision shall be made for steering in the event of a breakdown in the main steering arrangements.

Regulation 45
Computation for freeboard

[P88] **(1)** The minimum summer freeboards shall be computed in accordance with regulations 27(5), 27(6), 27(14), 28, 29, 30, 31, 32, 37 and 38, except that regulation 37 is modified by substituting the following percentages for those given in regulation 37:

[P88] **Table 45.1**

	Total effective length of superstructure										
	0	$0.1L$	$0.2L$	$0.3L$	$0.4L$	$0.5L$	$0.6L$	$0.7L$	$0.8L$	$0.9L$	$1.0L$
Percentage of deduction for all types of superstructure	20	31	42	53	64	70	76	82	88	94	100

[P88] Percentages at intermediate lengths of superstructure shall be obtained by linear interpolation.

(2) The Winter Timber freeboard shall be obtained by adding to the Summer Timber freeboard one thirty-sixth of the moulded summer timber draught.

(3) The Winter North Atlantic Timber freeboard shall be the same as the Winter North Atlantic freeboard prescribed in regulation 40(6).

(4) The Tropical Timber freeboard shall be obtained by deducting from the Summer Timber freeboard one forty-eighth of the moulded summer timber draught.

P88 **(5)** The Fresh Water Timber freeboard shall be computed in accordance with regulation 40(7), based on the summer timber load waterline, or with regulation 40(8), based on the summer timber draught measured from the top of the keel to the summer timber load line.

P88 **(6)** Timber freeboards may be assigned to ships with reduced type 'B' freeboards, provided the timber freeboards are calculated on the basis of the ordinary type 'B' freeboard.

P88 **(7)** The Timber Winter mark and/or the Timber Winter North Atlantic mark shall be placed at the same level as the reduced type 'B' Winter mark when the computed Timber Winter mark and/or the computed Timber Winter North Atlantic mark fall below the reduced type 'B' Winter mark.

Annex II
Zones, areas and seasonal periods

The zones and areas in this annex are, in general, based on the following criteria:

SUMMER   –   not more than 10% winds of force 8 Beaufort (34 knots) or more.

TROPICAL   –   not more than 1% winds of force 8 Beaufort (34 knots) or more. Not more than one tropical storm in 10 years in an area of 5° square in any one separate calendar month.

In certain special areas, for practical reasons, some degree of relaxation has been found acceptable.

A chart is attached to this annex to illustrate the zones and areas defined below.

Regulation 46
Northern Winter Seasonal Zones and Area

(1)   North Atlantic Winter Seasonal Zones I and II

(a)   The North Atlantic Winter Seasonal Zone I lies within the meridian of longitude 50° W from the coast of Greenland to latitude 45° N, thence the parallel of latitude 45° N to longitude 15° W, thence the meridian of longitude 15° W to latitude 60° N, thence the parallel of latitude 60° N to the Greenwich Meridian, thence this meridian northwards.

Seasonal periods:

WINTER: 16 October to 15 April
SUMMER: 16 April to 15 October

(b)   The North Atlantic Winter Seasonal Zone II lies within the meridian of longitude 68°30′ W from the coast of the United States to latitude 40° N, thence the rhumb line to the point latitude 36° N, longitude 73° W, thence the parallel of latitude 36° N to longitude 25° W and thence the rhumb line to Cape Toriñana.

P88 Excluded from this zone are the North Atlantic Winter Seasonal Zone I, the North Atlantic Winter Seasonal Area and the Baltic Sea bounded by the parallel of latitude of The Skaw in the Skagerrak. The Shetland Islands are to be considered as being on the boundary of the North Atlantic Winter Seasonal Zones I and II.

Seasonal periods:

> WINTER: 1 November to 31 March
> SUMMER: 1 April to 31 October

(2) North Atlantic Winter Seasonal Area

The boundary of the North Atlantic Winter Seasonal Area is

> the meridian of longitude 68°30′ W from the coast of the United States to latitude 40° N, thence the rhumb line to the southernmost intersection of the meridian of longitude 61° W with the coast of Canada and thence the east coasts of Canada and the United States.

Seasonal periods:

For ships over 100 m in length:

> WINTER: 16 December to 15 February
> SUMMER: 16 February to 15 December

For ships of 100 m and under in length:

> WINTER: 1 November to 31 March
> SUMMER: 1 April to 31 October

(3) North Pacific Winter Seasonal Zone

The southern boundary of the North Pacific Winter Seasonal Zone is

> the parallel of latitude 50° N from the east coast of the USSR to the west coast of Sakhalin, thence the west coast of Sakhalin to the southern extremity of Cape Kril'on, thence the rhumb line to Wakkanai, Hokkaido, Japan, thence the east and south coasts of Hokkaido to longitude 145° E, thence the meridian of longitude 145° E to latitude 35° N, thence the parallel of latitude 35° N to longitude 150° W and thence the rhumb line to the southern extremity of Dall Island, Alaska.

Seasonal periods:

> WINTER: 16 October to 15 April
> SUMMER: 16 April to 15 October

Regulation 47
Southern Winter Seasonal Zone

The northern boundary of the Southern Winter Seasonal Zone is

P88   the rhumb line from the east coast of the American continent at Cape Tres Puntas to the point latitude 34° S, longitude 50° W, thence the parallel of latitude 34° S to longitude 17° E, thence the rhumb line to the point latitude 35°10′ S, longitude 20° E, thence the rhumb line to the point latitude 34° S, longitude 28° E, thence along the rhumb line to the point latitude 35°30′ S, longitude 118° E, and thence the rhumb line to Cape Grim on the north-west coast of Tasmania; thence along the north and east coasts of Tasmania to the southernmost point of Bruny Island, thence the rhumb line to Black Rock Point on Stewart

Island, thence the rhumb line to the point latitude 47° S, longitude 170° E, thence along the rhumb line to the point latitude 33° S, longitude 170° W, and thence the parallel of latitude 33° S to the point latitude 33° S, longitude 79° W, thence the rhumb line to the point latitude 41° S, longitude 75° W, thence the rhumb line to Punta Corona lighthouse on Chiloe Island, latitude 41°47′ S, longitude 73°53′ W, thence along the north, east and south coasts of Chiloe Island to the point latitude 43°20′ S, longitude 74°20′ W, and thence the meridian of longitude 74°20′ W to the parallel of latitude 45°45′ S, including the inner zone of Chiloe channels from the meridian 74°20′ W to the east.

Seasonal periods:

WINTER: 16 April to 15 October
SUMMER: 16 October to 15 April

Regulation 48
Tropical Zone

(1)   Northern boundary of the Tropical Zone

The northern boundary of the Tropical Zone is

the parallel of latitude 13° N from the east coast of the American continent to longitude 60° W, thence the rhumb line to the point latitude 10° N, longitude 58° W, thence the parallel of latitude 10° N to longitude 20° W, thence the meridian of longitude 20° W to latitude 30° N and thence the parallel of latitude 30° N to the west coast of Africa; from the east coast of Africa the parallel of latitude 8° N to longitude 70° E, thence the meridian of longitude 70° E to latitude 13° N, thence the parallel of latitude 13° N to the west coast of India; thence the south coast of India to latitude 10°30′ N on the east coast of India, thence the rhumb line to the point latitude 9° N, longitude 82° E, thence the meridian of longitude 82° E to latitude 8° N, thence the parallel of latitude 8° N to the west coast of Malaysia, thence the coast of South-East Asia to the east coast of Viet Nam at latitude 10° N, thence the parallel of latitude 10° N to longitude 145° E, thence the meridian of longitude 145° E to latitude 13° N and thence the parallel of latitude 13° N to the west coast of the American continent.

Saigon is to be considered as being on the boundary line of the Tropical Zone and the Seasonal Tropical Area.

(2)   Southern boundary of the Tropical Zone

The southern boundary of the Tropical Zone is

the rhumb line from the Port of Santos, Brazil, to the point where the meridian of longitude 40° W intersects the Tropic of Capricorn; thence the Tropic of Capricorn to the west coast of Africa; from the east coast of Africa the parallel of latitude 20° S to the west coast of Madagascar, thence the west and north coasts of Madagascar to longitude 50° E, thence the meridian of longitude 50° E to latitude

177

10° S, thence the parallel of latitude 10° S to longitude 98° E, thence the rhumb line to Port Darwin, Australia, thence the coasts of Australia and Wessel Island eastwards to Cape Wessel, thence the parallel of latitude 11° S to the west side of Cape York; from the east side of Cape York the parallel of latitude 11° S to longitude 150° W, thence the rhumb line to the point latitude 26° S, longitude 75° W, thence the rhumb line to the point latitude 32°47' S, longitude 72° W, and thence to the parallel of latitude 32°47' S to the west coast of South America.

[P88] Valparaiso and Santos are to be considered as being on the boundary line of the Tropical and Summer Zones.

(3) Areas to be included in the Tropical Zone

The following areas are to be treated as included in the Tropical Zone:

(a) The Suez Canal, the Red Sea and the Gulf of Aden, from Port Said to the meridian of longitude 45° E.

Aden and Berbera are to be considered as being on the boundary line of the Tropical Zone and the Seasonal Tropical Area.

(b) The Persian Gulf to the meridian of longitude 59° E.

(c) The area bounded by the parallel of latitude 22° S from the east coast of Australia to the Great Barrier Reef, thence the Great Barrier Reef to latitude 11° S. The northern boundary of the area is the southern boundary of the Tropical Zone.

Regulation 49
Seasonal tropical areas

The following are Seasonal Tropical Areas:

(1) In the North Atlantic

An area bounded

on the north by the rhumb line from Cape Catoche, Yucatan, to Cape San Antonio, Cuba, the north coast of Cuba to latitude 20° N and thence the parallel of latitude 20° N to longitude 20° W;

on the west by the coast of the American continent;

on the south and east by the northern boundary of the Tropical Zone.

Sasonal periods:

TROPICAL: 1 November to 15 July
SUMMER: 16 July to 31 October

(2) In the Arabian Sea

An area bounded

on the west by the coast of Africa, the meridian of longitude 45° E in the Gulf of Aden, the coast of South Arabia and the meridian of longitude 59° E in the Gulf of Oman;

on the north and east by the coasts of Pakistan and India;

on the south by the northern boundary of the Tropical Zone.

Seasonal periods:

TROPICAL: 1 September to 31 May
SUMMER: 1 June to 31 August

(3)   In the Bay of Bengal

The Bay of Bengal north of the northern boundary of the Tropical Zone.

Seasonal periods:

TROPICAL: 1 December to 30 April
SUMMER: 1 May to 30 November

(4)   In the South Indian Ocean

(a)   An area bounded

on the north and west by the southern boundary of the Tropical Zone and the east coast of Madagascar;

on the south by the parallel of latitude 20° S;

on the east by the rhumb line from the point latitude 20° S, longitude 50° E, to the point latitude 15° S, longitude 51°30′ E, and thence by the meridian of longitude 51°30′ E to latitude 10° S.

Seasonal periods:

TROPICAL: 1 April to 30 November
SUMMER: 1 December to 31 March

(b)   An area bounded

on the north by the southern boundary of the Tropical Zone;

on the east by the coast of Australia;

P88   on the south by the parallel of latitude 15° S from longitude 51°30′ E to longitude 114° E and thence the meridian of longitude 114° E to the coast of Australia;

on the west by the meridian of longitude 51°30′ E.

Seasonal periods:

TROPICAL: 1 May to 30 November
SUMMER: 1 December to 30 April

(5)   In the China Sea

An area bounded

on the west and north by the coasts of Viet Nam and China from latitude 10° N to Hong Kong;

on the east by the rhumb line from Hong Kong to the Port of Sual (Luzon Island) and the west coasts of the Islands of Luzon, Samar, and Leyte to latitude 10° N;

on the south by the parallel of latitude 10° N.

Hong Kong and Sual are to be considered as being on the boundary of the Seasonal Tropical Area and Summer Zone.

Seasonal periods:

TROPICAL: 21 January to 30 April
SUMMER: 1 May to 20 January

(6)   In the North Pacific

(a)   An area bounded

on the north by the parallel of latitude 25° N;

on the west by the meridian of longitude 160° E;

on the south by the parallel of latitude 13° N;

on the east by the meridian of longitude 130° W.

Seasonal periods:

TROPICAL: 1 April to 31 October
SUMMER: 1 November to 31 March

(b)   An area bounded

on the north and east by the west coast of the American continent;

on the west by the meridian of longitude 123° W from the coast of the American continent to latitude 33° N and by the rhumb line from the point latitude 33° N, longitude 123° W, to the point latitude 13° N, longitude 105° W;

on the south by the parallel of latitude 13° N.

Seasonal periods:

TROPICAL: 1 March to 30 June and 1 November to 30 November
SUMMER: 1 July to 31 October and 1 December to 28/29 February.

(7)   In the South Pacific

(a)   The Gulf of Carpentaria south of latitude 11° S.

Seasonal periods:

TROPICAL: 1 April to 30 November
SUMMER: 1 December to 31 March

(b)   An area bounded

on the north and east by the southern boundary of the Tropical Zone;

on the south by the parallel of latitude of 24° S from the east coast of Australia to longitude 154° E, thence by the meridian of longitude 154° E to the Tropic of Capricorn and thence by the Tropic of Capricorn to longitude 150° W, thence by the meridian of longitude 150° W to latitude 20° S and thence by the parallel of latitude 20° S to the point where it intersects the southern boundary of the Tropical Zone; and

on the west by the boundaries of the area within the Great Barrier Reef included in the Tropical Zone and by the east coast of Australia.

Seasonal periods:

TROPICAL: 1 April to 30 November
SUMMER: 1 December to 31 March

Regulation 50
Summer Zones

The remaining areas constitute the Summer Zones.

However, for ships of 100 m and under in length, the area bounded

on the north and west by the east coast of the United States;

on the east by the meridian of longitude 68°30′ W from the coast of the United States to latitude 40° N and thence by the rhumb line to the point latitude 36° N, longitude 73° W;

on the south by the parallel of latitude 36° N

is a Winter Seasonal Area.

Seasonal periods:

WINTER: 1 November to 31 March
SUMMER: 1 April to 31 October

Regulation 51
Enclosed seas

(1)   Baltic Sea

This sea bounded by the parallel of latitude of The Skaw in the Skagerrak is included in the Summer Zones.

However, for ships of 100 m and under in length, it is a Winter Seasonal Area.

Seasonal periods:

WINTER: 1 November to 31 March
SUMMER: 1 April to 31 October

(2)   Black Sea

This sea is included in the Summer Zones.

However, for ships of 100 m and under in length, the area north of latitude 44° N is a Winter Seasonal Area.

Seasonal periods:

> WINTER: 1 December to 28/29 February
> SUMMER: 1 March to 30 November

(3)   Mediterranean

This sea is included in the Summer Zones.

However, for ships of 100 m and under in length, the area bounded
> on the north and west by the coasts of France and Spain and the meridian of longitude 3° E from the coast of Spain to latitude 40° N;
> on the south by the parallel of latitude 40° N from longitude 3° E to the west coast of Sardinia;
> on the east by the west and north coasts of Sardinia from latitude 40° N to longitude 9° E, thence by the meridian of longitude 9° E to the south coast of Corsica, thence by the west and north coasts of Corsica to longitude 9° E and thence by the rhumb line to Cape Sicié

is a Winter Seasonal Area.

Seasonal periods:

> WINTER: 16 December to 15 March
> SUMMER: 16 March to 15 December

(4)   Sea of Japan

This sea south of latitude 50° N is included in the Summer Zones.

However, for ships of 100 m and under in length, the area between the parallel of latitude 50° N and the rhumb line from the east coast of Korea at latitude 38° N to the west coast of Hokkaido, Japan, at latitude 43°12′ N is a Winter Seasonal Area.

Seasonal periods:

> WINTER: 1 December to 28/29 February
> SUMMER: 1 March to 30 November

Regulation 52
The Winter North Atlantic Load Line

The part of the North Atlantic referred to in regulation 40(6) (annex I) comprises:

> **(a)** that part of the North Atlantic Winter Seasonal Zone II which lies between the meridians of 15° W and 50° W;
>
> **(b)** the whole of the North Atlantic Winter Seasonal Zone I, the Shetland Islands to be considered as being on the boundary.

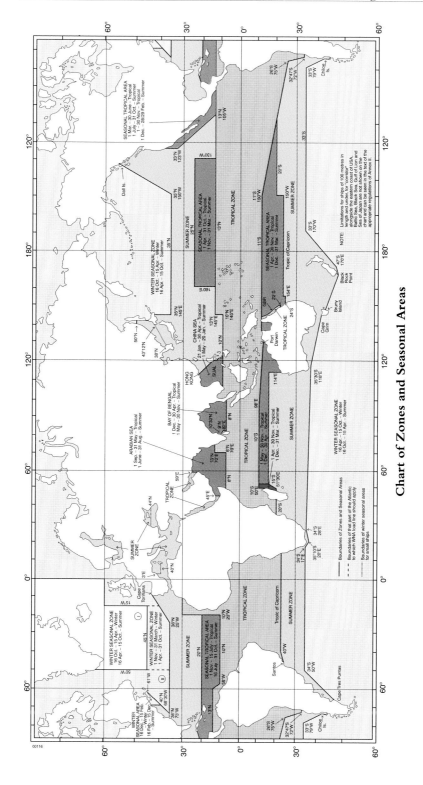

Chart of Zones and Seasonal Areas

183

Annex III
Certificates

P88 Form of International Certificate on Load Lines

P88 INTERNATIONAL LOAD LINE CERTIFICATE

(Official seal)   *(State)*

Issued under the provisions of the
INTERNATIONAL CONVENTION ON LOAD LINES, 1966,
as modified by the Protocol of 1988 relating thereto

under the authority of the Government of

_____
(name of the State)

by _____
(person or organization authorized)

Particulars of ship[1]

Name of ship . . . .

Distinctive number or letters . . . .

Port of registry . . . .

Length (*L*) as defined in article 2(8) (in metres). . . . .

IMO Number[2] . . . .

---

[1] Alternatively, the particulars of the ship may be placed horizontally in boxes.
[2] In accordance with resolution A.600(15) – IMO Ship Identification Number Scheme, this information may be included voluntarily.

Freeboard assigned as:[3]	Type of ship[3]
A new ship	Type 'A' Type 'B'
An existing ship	Type 'B' with reduced freeboard Type 'B' with increased freeboard

Freeboard from deck line[4]		**Load line**
Tropical	. . . . mm (T)	. . . . mm above (S)
Summer	. . . . mm (S)	Upper edge of line through centre of ring
Winter	. . . . mm (W)	. . . . mm below (S)
Winter North Atlantic	. . . . mm (WNA)	. . . . mm below (S)
Timber tropical	. . . . mm (LT)	. . . . mm above (LS)
Timber summer	. . . . mm (LS)	. . . . mm above (S)
Timber winter	. . . . mm (LW)	. . . . mm below (LS)
Timber winter North Atlantic	. . . . mm (LWNA)	. . . . mm below (LS)

Allowance for fresh water for all freeboards other than timber . . . . mm. For timber freeboards . . . . mm.

The upper edge of the deck line from which these freeboards are measured is . . . . mm . . . . deck at side.

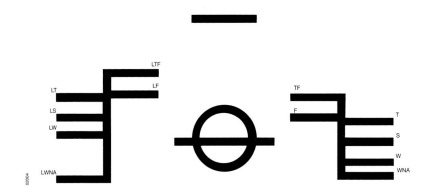

---

[3] Delete as appropriate.
[4] Freeboards and load lines which are not applicable need not be entered on the certificate. Subdivision load lines may be entered on the certificate on a voluntary basis.

THIS IS TO CERTIFY:

1   That the ship has been surveyed in accordance with the requirements of article 14 of the Convention.

2   That the survey showed that the freeboards have been assigned and load lines shown above have been marked in accordance with the Convention.

This certificate is valid until . . . .[5] subject to annual surveys in accordance with article 14(1)(c) of the Convention.[6]

Issued at . . . .
(Place of issue of certificate)

. . . .
(Date of issue)   *(Signature of authorized official issuing the certificate)*

(Seal or stamp of the authority, as appropriate)

NOTES: 1 When a ship departs from a port situated on a river or inland waters, deeper loading shall be permitted corresponding to the weight of fuel and all other materials required for consumption between the point of departure and the sea.

2 When a ship is in fresh water of unit density the appropriate load line may be submerged by the amount of fresh water allowance shown above. Where the density is other than unity, an allowance shall be made proportional to the difference between 1.025 and the actual density.

---

[5] Insert the date of expiry as specified by the Administration in accordance with article 19(1) of the Convention. The day and the month of this date correspond to the anniversary date as defined in article 2(9) of the Convention, unless amended in accordance with article 19(8) of the Convention.
[6] See resolution MSC.172(79), in part 4 of this publication.

Endorsement for annual surveys

THIS IS TO CERTIFY that, at an annual survey required by article 14(1)(c) of the Convention, the ship was found to comply with the relevant requirements of the Convention.

Annual survey:

Signed: . . . .
(Signature of authorized official)

Place: . . . .

Date: . . . .

(Seal or stamp of the authority, as appropriate)

Annual survey:

Signed: . . . .
(Signature of authorized official)

Place: . . . .

Date: . . . .

(Seal or stamp of the authority, as appropriate)

Annual survey:

Signed: . . . .
(Signature of authorized official)

Place: . . . .

Date: . . . .

(Seal or stamp of the authority, as appropriate)

Annual survey:

Signed: . . . .
(Signature of authorized official)

Place: . . . .

Date: . . . .

(Seal or stamp of the authority, as appropriate)

Annual survey in accordance with article 19(8)(c)

THIS IS TO CERTIFY that, at a survey in accordance with article 19(8)(c) of the Convention, the ship was found to comply with the relevant requirements of the Convention.

Signed: . . . .
(Signature of authorized official)

Place: . . . .

Date: . . . .

(Seal or stamp of the authority, as appropriate)

Endorsement to extend the certificate if valid for less than 5 years where article 19(3) applies

The ship complies with the relevant requirements of the Convention, and this certificate shall, in accordance with article 19(3) of the Convention, be accepted as valid until . . . .

Signed: . . . .
(Signature of authorized official)

Place: . . . .

Date: . . . .

(Seal or stamp of the authority, as appropriate)

Endorsement where the renewal survey has been completed and article 19(4) applies

The ship complies with the relevant requirements of the Convention, and this certificate shall, in accordance with article 19(4) of the Convention, be accepted as valid until . . . .

Signed: . . . .
(Signature of authorized official)

Place: . . . .

Date: . . . .

(Seal or stamp of the authority, as appropriate)

Endorsement to extend the validity of the certificate until reaching the port of survey or for a period of grace where article 19(5) or 19(6) applies

This certificate shall, in accordance with article 19(5)/19(6)[3] of the Convention, be accepted as valid until . . . .

Signed: . . . .
(Signature of authorized official)

Place: . . . .

Date: . . . .

(Seal or stamp of the authority, as appropriate)

Endorsement for advancement of anniversary date where article 19(8) applies

In accordance with article 19(8) of the Convention the new anniversary date is
. . . .

Signed: . . . .
(Signature of authorized official)

Place: . . . .

Date: . . . .

(Seal or stamp of the authority, as appropriate)

In accordance with article 19(8) of the Convention the new anniversary date is
. . . .

Signed: . . . .
(Signature of authorized official)

Place: . . . .

Date: . . . .

(Seal or stamp of the authority, as appropriate)

---

[3] Delete as appropriate.

P88 Form of International Exemption Certificate on Load Lines

P88 INTERNATIONAL LOAD LINE EXEMPTION CERTIFICATE

(Official seal)   *(State)*

Issued under the provisions of the
INTERNATIONAL CONVENTION ON LOAD LINES, 1966,
as modified by the Protocol of 1988 relating thereto

under the authority of the Government of

_____

(name of the State)

by   _____

(person or organization authorized)

Particulars of ship[1]

Name of ship . . . .

Distinctive number or letters . . . .

Port of registry . . . .

Length (L) as defined in article 2(8) (in metres) . . . .

IMO Number[2] . . . .

_____

[1] Alternatively, the particulars of the ship may be placed horizontally in boxes.
[2] In accordance with resolution A.600(15), IMO Ship Identification Number Scheme, this information may be included voluntarily.

THIS IS TO CERTIFY:

That the ship is exempted from the provisions of the Convention, under the authority conferred by article 6(2)/6(4)[3] of the Convention referred to above.

The provisions of the Convention from which the ship is exempted under article 6(2) are:

. . . .

. . . .

. . . .

The voyage for which exemption is granted under article 6(4) is:

From: . . . .

To: . . . .

Conditions, if any, on which the exemption is granted under either article 6(2) or article 6(4):

. . . .

. . . .

. . . .

This certificate is valid until . . . .[4] subject to annual surveys in accordance with article 14(1)(c) of the Convention.[5]

Issued at . . . .
(Place of issue of certificate)

. . . .
(Date of issue)   *(Signature of authorized official issuing the certificate)*

(Seal or stamp of the authority, as appropriate)

---

[3] Delete as appropriate.

[4] Insert the date of expiry as specified by the Administration in accordance with article 19(10) of the Convention. The day and the month of this date correspond to the anniversary date as defined in article 2(9) of the Convention, unless amended in accordance with article 19(8) of the Convention.

[5] See resolution MSC.172(79), in part 4 of this publication.

Endorsement for annual surveys

THIS IS TO CERTIFY that, at an annual survey required by article 14(1)(c) of the Convention, the ship was found to comply with the conditions under which this exemption was granted.

Annual survey:

Signed: . . . .
(Signature of authorized official)

Place: . . . .

Date: . . . .

(Seal or stamp of the authority, as appropriate)

Annual survey:

Signed: . . . .
(Signature of authorized official)

Place: . . . .

Date: . . . .

(Seal or stamp of the authority, as appropriate)

Annual survey:

Signed: . . . .
(Signature of authorized official)

Place: . . . .

Date: . . . .

(Seal or stamp of the authority, as appropriate)

Annual survey:

Signed: . . . .
(Signature of authorized official)

Place: . . . .

Date: . . . .

(Seal or stamp of the authority, as appropriate)

Annual survey in accordance with article 19(8)(c)

THIS IS TO CERTIFY that, at a survey required by article 19(8)(c) of the Convention, the ship was found to comply with the relevant requirements of the Convention.

Signed: . . . .
(Signature of authorized official)

Place: . . . .

Date: . . . .

(Seal or stamp of the authority, as appropriate)

Endorsement to extend the certificate if valid for less than 5 years and where article 19(3) applies

The ship complies with the relevant requirements of the Convention, and this certificate shall, in accordance with article 19(3) of the Convention, be accepted as valid until . . . .

Signed: . . . .
(Signature of authorized official)

Place: . . . .

Date: . . . .

(Seal or stamp of the authority, as appropriate)

Endorsement where the renewal survey has been completed and article 19(4) applies

The ship complies with the relevant requirements of the Convention, and this certificate shall, in accordance with article 19(4) of the Convention, be accepted as valid until . . . .

Signed: . . . .
(Signature of authorized official)

Place: . . . .

Date: . . . .

(Seal or stamp of the authority, as appropriate)

Endorsement to extend the validity of the certificate until reaching the port of survey or for a period of grace where article 19(5) or 19(6) applies

This certificate shall, in accordance with article 19(5)/19(6)[3] of the Convention, be accepted as valid until . . . .

Signed: . . . .
(Signature of authorized official)

Place: . . . .

Date: . . . .

(Seal or stamp of the authority, as appropriate)

Endorsement for advancement of anniversary date where article 19(8) applies

In accordance with article 19(8) of the Convention the new anniversary date is . . . .

Signed: . . . .
(Signature of authorized official)

Place: . . . .

Date: . . . .

(Seal or stamp of the authority, as appropriate)

In accordance with article 19(8) of the Convention the new anniversary date is . . . .

Signed: . . . .
(Signature of authorized official)

Place: . . . .

Date: . . . .

(Seal or stamp of the authority, as appropriate)

---

[3] Delete as appropriate.

Part 4
Amendments to the 1988 Protocol that have not yet been accepted by sufficient parties to be able to come into force

AMENDMENTS TO THE PROTOCOL OF 1988 RELATING TO THE INTERNATIONAL CONVENTION ON LOAD LINES, 1966

These amendments were adopted by resolution MSC.172(79) on 9 December 2004. Although adopted, in accordance with paragraph 2(d) of article VI of the 1988 Load Lines Protocol, and circulated to all Contracting Governments, these amendments can only come into force on 1 July 2006 after they have been accepted by sufficient Contracting Governments. They will be deemed to have been accepted on 1 January 2006 unless, prior to that date, more than one third of the Parties to the 1988 Load Lines Protocol, or Parties the combined merchant fleets of which constitute not less than 50% of the gross tonnage of the world's merchant fleet, have notified their objections.

AMENDMENTS TO ANNEX B TO THE PROTOCOL OF 1988 RELATING TO THE INTERNATIONAL CONVENTION ON LOAD LINES, 1966

Annex III
Certificates

Form of International Certificate on Load Lines

1   In the form of the International Load Line Certificate, the following new section is inserted between the section commencing with the words "This certificate is valid until" and the section commencing with the words "Issued at":

"Completion date of the survey on which this certificate is based: . . . . "
(dd/mm/yyyy)

Form of International Exemption Certificate on Load Lines

2   In the form of the International Load Line Exemption Certificate, the following new section is inserted between the section commencing with the words "This certificate is valid until" and the section commencing with the words "Issued at":

"Completion date of the survey on which this certificate is based: . . . . "
(dd/mm/yyyy)

Part 5
Unified interpretations of the provisions of the International Convention on Load Lines, 1966

In applying the articles and regulations of the 1966 Load Line Convention, the following interpretations are recommended to Contracting Governments in order to ensure the uniform application of the relevant articles and regulations.

Definition of length for a segmented ship *(article 2(8))*

A ship which is composed of a series of permanently attached sections should have a freeboard determined by the overall length of the series. A rigidly attached, but detachable, propulsion section should be included in the total length (L). A non-rigidly attached, detachable propulsion section should be treated as a separate ship.

Application *(article 4(4))*
(IACS interpretation LL.1)

Even where the increase in draught is only of the order of 25 mm or 50 mm there should be no relaxation from the condition that existing ships comply with all the requirements.

Exemptions *(article 6)*

An exemption certificate according to article 6 should be granted by the Administration for ships whose operational features lead to submergence of the load line mark during loading or unloading, to avoid contravention of article 12(1).

Form of certificates *(article 18)*
(IACS interpretation LL.19)

The model form of certificates given in annex III of the Load Line Convention should be strictly adhered to and any deviations from this pattern should be avoided.

Freeboards greater than minimum *(regulation 2(5))*
(IACS interpretation LL.51)

Where freeboards are required to be increased, because of such considerations as strength (regulation 1), location of shell doors (regulation 21) or sidescuttles (regulation 23) or other reasons, then:

  .1 the height of
  – door sills (regulation 12)
  – hatchway coamings (regulation 15(1))
  – sills of machinery space openings (regulation 17)
  – miscellaneous openings (regulation 18)
  – ventilators (regulation 19)
  – air pipes (regulation 20)

  .2 the scantlings of hatch covers (regulations 15 and 16)

  .3 freeing arrangements (regulation 24) and means for protection of crew (regulation 25) on the actual freeboard deck may be as required for a superstructure deck, provided the summer freeboard is such that the resulting draught will not be greater than that corresponding to the minimum freeboard calculated from an assumed freeboard deck situated at a distance equal to a standard super-structure height below the actual freeboard deck. Similar considerations may be given in cases of draught limitation on account of bow height (regulation 39).

Moulded depth *(regulation 3(5)(c) and (9))* **and freeboard calculation** *(regulation 40(1))*

Discontinuous freeboard deck, stepped freeboard deck (IACS interpretation LL.48/Rev.1)

1 Where a step exists in the freeboard deck, creating a discontinuity extending over the full breadth of the ship, and this step is in excess of 1 m in length, regulation 3(9) should apply (figure 1). A step 1 m or less in length should be treated as a recess in accordance with paragraph 2.

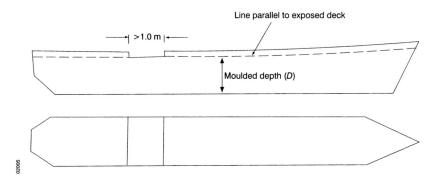

Figure 1

2 Where a recess is arranged in the freeboard deck, and this recess does not extend to the side of the ship, the freeboard calculated without regard to the recess is to be corrected for the consequent loss of buoyancy. The correction should be equal to the value obtained by dividing the volume of the recess by the waterplane area of the ship (A_W) at 85% of the least moulded depth (figure 2):

.1 The correction should be a straight addition to the freeboard obtained after all other corrections have been applied, except bow height correction.

.2 Where the freeboard, corrected for lost buoyancy as above, is greater than the minimum geometric freeboard determined on the basis of a moulded depth measured to the bottom of the recess, the latter value may be used.

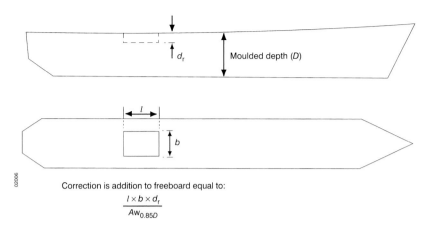

Correction is addition to freeboard equal to:

$$\frac{l \times b \times d_r}{Aw_{0.85D}}$$

Figure 2

3   Recesses in a second deck, designated as the freeboard deck, may be disregarded in this interpretation provided all openings in the weather deck are fitted with weathertight closing appliances.

4   Due regard is to be given to the drainage of exposed recesses and to free surface effects on stability.

5   This interpretation is not intended to apply to dredgers, hopper barges or other similar types of ships with large open holds, where each case should require individual consideration.

Depth for freeboard *(regulation 3(6))*
(IACS interpretation LL.2)

The correction for thickness of sheathing on the exposed freeboard deck, $\dfrac{T(L-S)}{L}$ is applicable only when the deck is completely sheathed between superstructures. In other cases the correction should be $\dfrac{T \times l}{L}$ where l = length of sheathed area which extends from side to side. Only wood sheathing should be considered.

Structure of a lower freeboard deck *(regulation 3(9))*
(IACS interpretation LL.39)

When a lower deck is designated as the freeboard deck, it should be continuous in fore and aft direction as well as athwartship. Such freeboard deck as a minimum should consist of suitably framed stringers at the ship sides and transversely at each watertight bulkhead which extends to the upper deck, within cargo spaces. The width of these stringers should not be less than can be conveniently fitted having regard to the structure and the operation of the ship. Any arrangement of stringers should be such that structural requirement can also be met.

See also the interpretation of regulations 3(5)(c) and (9) and 40(1)

Superstructure *(regulation 3(10)(b))*
(IACS interpretation LL.3)

A bridge or poop should not be regarded as enclosed unless access is provided for the crew starting from any point on the uppermost complete exposed deck or higher to reach machinery and other working spaces inside these superstructures by alternative means which are available at all times when bulkhead openings are closed.

Details of marking *(regulation 8)*
(IACS interpretation LL.4)

"Permanently marked" is considered to include welding of the marks on the sides of the ship provided the usual precautions as to material, electrodes, etc. are observed.

Doors *(regulation 12)*
(IACS interpretation LL.5)

Doors should generally open outwards to provide additional security against the impact of the sea. Doors which open inwards should be exceptionally approved.

Portable sills should be avoided. However, in order to facilitate the loading/ unloading of heavy or bulky spare parts, portable sills may be fitted on the following conditions:

.1 that they are installed before the ship leaves port;

.2 that they are gasketted and fastened by closely spaced through bolts.

Whenever the sills are replaced after removal, the weathertightness of the sills and related doors should be verified by hose testing. The dates of removal, replacing and hose testing should be recorded in the ship's log-book.

Hatch beams and cover stiffeners of variable cross-section *(regulations 15(4), (5), (6), (7) and 16))*
(IACS interpretation LL.20)

To avoid stresses and deflections exceeding those given in the above regulations along construction elements of variable cross-section, the required section modulus calculated as for construction elements of constant cross-section should be increased by a factor K expressed by:

$$K = 1 + \frac{3.2\alpha - \gamma - 0.8}{7\gamma + 0.4}$$

where $\alpha = l_1/l_0$, $\gamma = W_1/W_0$

The value of factor K obtained by the formula should be not less than unity.

l_1, l_0, W_1 and W_0 are indicated in the figure 3 below:

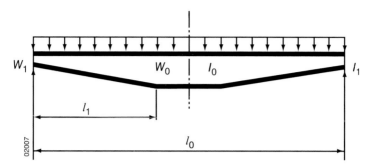

Figure 3

The moment of inertia should likewise be increased by the factor C expressed by:

$$C = 1 + 8\alpha^3 \frac{1 - \beta}{0.2 + 3\sqrt{\beta}}$$

where $\alpha = l_1/l_0$, $\beta = I_1/I_0$

The value of factor C obtained by the formula should be not less than unity.

I_1 and I_0 are indicated in figure 3 above.

The use of the above formulae should be limited to the determination of the strength of hatch beams and covers in which abrupt changes in the section of the face material do not occur along the length of the beam or cover.

Security of hatchway covers *(regulation 15(13))*
(IACS interpretation LL.40/Rev.1)

This interpretation is not intended to be applied to existing ships.

Acceptable equivalent means to steel bars should consist of devices and materials which could provide strength equivalent to, and elasticity not greater than that of, steel.

Steel wire ropes should not be regarded as satisfactory equivalent means.

Care should be taken to ensure that tarpaulins are adequately protected from the possibility of damage arising from the use of securing devices which do not provide a flat bearing surface.

Hatchways closed by weathertight covers of steel or other equivalent material fitted with gaskets and clamping devices *(regulations 16 and 27(7)(c))*
(IACS interpretation LL.6)

Regulation 16

Where hatchways are fitted with coamings of standard height, no extra strengthening (beyond what is required in the Convention) should be required for covers loaded with cargo, even dense cargo, provided the load does not exceed 1.75 tonnes/m^2 (in position 1).

Regulation 27(7)(c)

No extra strengthening is recommended for hatchway covers on ships which are assigned freeboards less than those based on table B, except for flush hatchway covers which are fitted on the freeboard deck forward of the quarter length, in which case the section modulus and the moment of inertia should be increased 15% over that required by regulation 16.

Machinery space openings *(regulations 17(1), 26(1), 27(9) and 27(10))*

Where casings are not protected by other structures, double doors should be required for type A or type B ships assigned freeboards less than those based on table B*. An inner sill of 230 mm in conjunction with the outer sill of 600 mm is recommended.

Machinery space and emergency generator room ventilator coaming heights *(regulations 17(2), 19(3) and 19(4))*
(IACS interpretation LL.58)

Regulation 17(2) requires that the coamings of machinery space ventilators situated in exposed positions on the freeboard and superstructure decks shall be as high above the deck as is reasonable and practicable.

In general, ventilators necessary to continuously supply the machinery space and, on demand, immediately supply the emergency generator room should have coamings which comply with regulation 19(3), without having to fit weathertight closing appliances.

However, where due to ship size and arrangement this is not practicable, lesser heights for machinery space and emergency generator room ventilator coamings may be accepted with the provision of weathertight closing appliances in accordance with regulation 19(4) in combination with other suitable arrangements to ensure an uninterrupted, adequate supply of ventilation to these spaces.

Miscellaneous openings in freeboard and superstructure decks *(regulation 18(2) and (3))*
(IACS interpretation LL.8)

Regulation 18(2)

Only those doorways in deckhouses leading to or giving access to companionways leading below, need to be fitted with doors in accordance with regulation 12.

Alternatively, if stairways within a deckhouse are enclosed within properly constructed companionways fitted with doors complying with regulation 12, then the external doors need not be weathertight.

Where an opening exists in a superstructure deck or in the top of a deckhouse on the freeboard deck which gives access to space below the freeboard deck or to a space within an enclosed superstructure and is protected by a deckhouse, then it is considered that only those sidescuttles fitted in spaces which give

---

* "Based on table B" means without any reduction in accordance with regulation 27(9) or (10).

direct access to an open stairway need be fitted with deadlights in accordance with regulation 23. A cabin is considered to provide adequate protection against the minimal amount of water which will enter through a broken sidescuttle glass fitted on the second tier.

Regulation 18(3)

In the application of regulation 18 it is understood that:

.1 where access is provided from the deck above as an alternative to access from the freeboard deck in accordance with regulation 3(10)(b) then the height of sills into a bridge or poop should be 380 mm. The same consideration should apply to deckhouses on the freeboard deck.

.2 where access is not provided from above, the height of the sills to doorways in a poop bridge or deckhouse on the freeboard deck should be 600 mm.

.3 where the closing appliances of access openings in superstructures and deckhouses are not in accordance with regulation 12, interior deck openings are to be considered exposed, i.e. situated in the open deck.

Protection of openings in raised quarter-decks *(regulations 18(2) and 23)*
(IACS interpretation LL.46/Rev.2)

By extension of regulation 23 and the interpretation of regulation 18(2) and (3) regarding miscellaneous openings in freeboard and superstructure decks, referred to above (see previous unified interpretation), deckhouses situated on a raised quarter-deck or on a superstructure of less than standard height may be treated as being on the second tier as far as the provision of deadlights and sidescuttles and windows is concerned, provided that the height of the raised quarter-deck or superstructure on which they are situated is equal to, or greater than, the standard quarter-deck height.

Regarding the requirement to protect openings in superstructures (regulation 18(2)), it is considered that openings in the top of a deckhouse on a raised quarter-deck or superstructure of less than standard height having a height equal to, or greater than, the standard quarter-deck height should be provided with an acceptable means of closing but need not be protected by an efficient deckhouse or companionway as defined in the regulation provided that the height of the deckhouse is at least the height of superstructure.

Minimum wall thickness of pipes *(regulations 19, 20 and 22)*
(IACS interpretation LL.36/Rev.1)

For pipes covered by the above regulations the following minimum wall thicknesses are recommended for those Administrations which do not have national regulations:

1   Scupper and discharge pipes, where substantial thickness is not required, and venting pipes other than specified in 3 below:

.1 For pipes having external diameter equal to or less than 155 mm thickness should not be less than 4.5 mm;

.2   For pipes having external diameter equal to or more than 230 mm thickness should not be less than 6 mm.

Intermediate sizes should be determined by linear interpolation.

2   Scupper and discharge pipes where substantial thickness is required:

.1   For pipes having external diameter equal to or less than 80 mm thickness should not be less than 7 mm;

.2   For pipes having external diameter of 180 mm thickness should not be less than 10 mm;

.3   For pipes having external diameter equal to or more than 220 mm thickness should not be less than 12.5 mm.

Intermediate sizes should be determined by linear interpolation.

3   Venting pipes in position 1 and 2 leading to spaces below the freeboard deck or to spaces within closed superstructures:

.1   For pipes having external diameter equal to or less than 80 mm thickness should not be less than 6 mm;

.2   For pipes having external diameter equal to or more than 165 mm thickness should not be less than 8.5 mm.

Intermediate sizes should be determined by linear interpolation.

See also the interpretation of regulations 17(2), 19(3) and 19(4)

Weathertight closing appliances for ventilators *(regulation 19(4))*
(IACS interpretation LL.52)

Where required by regulation 19, weathertight closing appliances for all ventilators in positions 1 and 2 are to be of steel or other equivalent materials.

Wood plugs and canvas covers are not acceptable in these positions.

Air pipes *(regulation 20)*
(IACS interpretation LL.10)

For ships assigned timber freeboards the air pipes should be provided with automatic closing appliances.

Air pipes *(regulation 20)*

In cases where air pipes are led through the side of superstructures, it is recommended that the height of their openings be more than 2.3 m above the summer load waterline.

Air pipe closing devices *(regulation 20)*
(IACS interpretation LL.49)

This interpretation is not intended to be applied to existing ships.

The means of closing air pipes should be weathertight and of an automatic type if the openings of the air pipes to which the devices are fitted would be submerged at an angle of less than 40° (or any lesser angle which may be needed to suit stability requirements) when the ship is floating at its summer load line draught. Pressure vacuum valves (P.V. valves) may be accepted on tankers.

Wooden plugs and trailing canvas hoses should not be accepted as closing devices for air pipes in positions 1 and 2.

Special requirements for vehicle ferries, ro-ro ships and other ships of similar type *(regulation 21)*
(IACS interpretation LL.32)

Stern, bow and side doors of large dimensions, when manual devices would not be readily accessible, should be normally secured by means of power systems. Alternative means of securing should also be provided for emergency use in case of failure of the power systems.

Cargo ports and other similar openings *(regulation 21(1))*

In a ship in which the lower deck has been designated as the freeboard deck, the means of closing openings in the shell plating below the weather deck but above the freeboard deck should be so designed as to ensure integrity against the sea commensurate with the surrounding shell plating, having regard to the position of the opening in relation to the waterline. In such a ship the following principles apply:

.1 the effectiveness of closing appliances fitted at cargo ports and other similar openings in the shell of a ship depends on regular observations and maintenance;

.2 hose tests are a practical means of verifying the weathertightness or watertightness of such closing appliances; and

.3 consideration should be given to the fitting of alarms giving warning of leakage in way of doors in exposed positions.

Cargo ports or similar openings below the uppermost load line *(regulation 21(2))*
(IACS interpretation LL.21)

Cargo ports or similar openings may be submerged provided the safety of the ship is in no way impaired. It is considered that the fitting of a second door of equivalent strength and watertightness is an acceptable arrangement. In this case a leakage detection device should be provided in the compartment between the two doors. Further, drainage of this compartment to the bilges controlled by an easily accessible screw-down valve, should be arranged. The outer door should preferably open outwards.

See also the interpretation of regulations 19, 20 and 22

Scuppers, inlets and discharges *(regulation 22(1))*
(IACS interpretation LL.11)

An acceptable equivalent to one automatic non-return valve with a positive means of closing from a position above the freeboard deck would be one automatic non-return valve and one sluice valve controlled from above the freeboard deck. Where two automatic non-return valves are required, the inboard valve should always be accessible under service conditions, i.e. the inboard valve should be above the level of the tropical load waterline. If this is not practicable, then, provided a locally controlled sluice valve is interposed between the two automatic non-return valves, the inboard valve need not be fitted above the load waterline.

Where sanitary discharges and scuppers lead overboard through the shell in way of manned machinery spaces, the fitting to shell of a locally operated positive closing valve together with a non-return valve inboard, is considered to provide protection equivalent to the requirements of regulation 22(1).

The requirements of regulation 22(1) for non-return valves should be applicable only to those discharges which remain open during the normal operation of a ship. For discharges which must necessarily be closed at sea, such as gravity drains from topside ballast tanks, a single screw-down valve operated from the deck is considered to provide efficient protection.

Position of the inboard end of discharges when a timber freeboard is assigned (regulation 22(1))
(IACS interpretation LL.22)

The position of the inboard end of discharges should be related to the timber summer load waterline when a timber freeboard is assigned.

Sidescuttles (regulation 23)
(IACS interpretation LL.12)

For those ships where the freeboard is reduced on account of subdivision characteristics, sidescuttles fitted outside the space considered flooded and which are below the final waterline should be of the non-opening type.

Sidescuttles, windows and skylights (regulation 23)
(IACS interpretation LL.62)

Sidescuttles and windows together with their glasses, deadlights* and storm covers*, if fitted, should be of approved design and substantial construction in accordance with, or equivalent to, recognized national or international standards. Non-metallic frames should not be acceptable.

Sidescuttles are defined as being round or oval openings with an area not exceeding 0.16 m^2. Round or oval openings having areas exceeding 0.16 m^2 should be treated as windows.

Windows are defined as being rectangular openings generally, having a radius at each corner relative to the window size in accordance with recognized national or international standards, and round or oval openings with an area exceeding 0.16 m^2.

Sidescuttles to the following spaces should be fitted with efficient hinged inside deadlights:

.1 spaces below freeboard deck;

.2 spaces within the first tier of enclosed superstructures; and

.3 first tier deckhouses on the freeboard deck protecting openings leading below or considered buoyant in stability calculations.

---

* Deadlights, in accordance with recognized standards, are fitted to the inside of windows and sidescuttles, while storm covers, of comparable specifications to deadlights, are fitted to the outside of windows, where accessible, and may be hinged or portable.

The deadlights should be capable of being effectively closed and secured watertight, if fitted below freeboard deck, and weathertight, if fitted above.

Sidescuttles should not be fitted in such a position that their sills are below a line drawn parallel to the freeboard deck at side and having its lowest point 2.5% of the breadth B, or 500 mm, whichever is the greatest distance, above the summer load line (or timber summer load line, if assigned).

Sidescuttles should be of the non-opening type in ships subject to damage stability regulations, if calculations indicate that they would become immersed by any intermediate stage of flooding or the final equilibrium waterplane in any required damage case.

Windows should not be fitted below the freeboard deck, in the first tier end bulkheads or sides of enclosed superstructures and in first tier deckhouses considered buoyant in the stability calculations or protecting openings leading below.

Sidescuttles and windows at the side shell in the second tier, protecting direct access below or considered buoyant in the stability calculations, should be provided with efficient hinged inside deadlights capable of being effectively closed and secured weathertight.

Sidescuttles and windows set inboard from the side shell in the second tier, protecting direct access below to spaces listed in paragraph 3.4 above, should be provided with either efficient hinged inside deadlights or, where they are accessible, permanently attached external storm covers of approved design and of substantial construction and capable of being effectively closed and secured weathertight.

Cabin bulkheads and doors in the second tier separating sidescuttles and windows from a direct access leading below may be accepted in place of deadlights or storm covers fitted to the sidescuttles and windows.

Deckhouses situated on a raised quarter-deck or on the deck of a superstructure of less than standard height may be regarded as being in the second tier as far as the provision of deadlights is concerned, provided the height of the raised quarter-deck or superstructure is equal to, or greater than, the standard quarter-deck height.

Fixed or opening skylights should have glass thickness appropriate to their size and position as required for sidescuttles and windows. Skylights glasses in any position should be protected from mechanical damage and, where fitted in position 1 or 2, should be provided with robust deadlights or storm covers permanently attached.

See also the interpretation of regulations 18(2) and 23

Freeing ports in way of wells in combination with open superstructures
(regulations 24(1) and 24(4))
(IACS interpretation LL.60)

In the case of ships having open superstructures on the freeboard or superstructure decks, which open to wells formed by bulwarks on the peripheries of the open decks, the Convention leaves to the satisfaction of the

213

Administration how the freeing port areas for the open spaces within the superstructures should be calculated.

Since water can enter only through the end bulkhead openings, the freeing port areas for the open spaces within the superstructures should be a function of the breadth of the end openings and the extent to which wells formed by the open decks and common spaces within the open superstructures are covered by the open superstructures.

To determine the minimum freeing port area on each side of the ship for the open superstructure (A_s) and for the open well (A_w), the following procedure is recommended:

> **.1** Determine the total well length (l_t) equal to the sum of the length of the open deck enclosed by bulwarks (l_w) and the length of the common space within the open superstructure (l_s).
>
> **.2** To determine A_s:
>
> > **.1** calculate the freeing port area (A) required for an open well of length l_t in accordance with regulation 24(1) with standard height bulwark assumed;
> >
> > **.2** multiply by the factor of 1.5 to correct for the absence of sheer, if applicable, in accordance with regulation 24(2);
> >
> > **.3** multiply by the factor (b_o/l_t) to adjust the freeing port area for the breadth (b_o) of the openings in the end bulkhead of the enclosed superstructure. (*Note:* This cancels the l_t terms from the calculation);
> >
> > **.4** to adjust the freeing port area for that part of the entire length of the well which is enclosed by the open superstructure, multiply by the factor:
> >
> > $$(1 - l_w/l_t^{2})$$
> >
> > where l_w and l_t are defined in 4.3.1 above;
> >
> > **.5** to adjust the freeing port area for the distance of the well deck above the freeboard deck, multiply by the factor:
> >
> > $$0.5(h_s/h_w)$$
> >
> > where h_w is the distance of the well deck above the freeboard deck and h_s is one standard superstructure height.
>
> **.3** To determine A_w:
>
> > **.1** the freeing port area for the open well (A_w) should be calculated in accordance with .2.1 above, using l_w to calculate (A') and then adjusted for the actual height of the bulwark (h_b) by the application of one of the following area corrections, whichever is applicable:
> >
> > > **.1.1** for bulwarks greater than 1.2 m in height:
> > >
> > > $$A_c = l_w (h_b - 1.2)/(0.1) (0.004) \text{ m}^2;$$
> > >
> > > **.1.2** for bulwarks less than 0.9 m in height:
> > >
> > > $$A_c = l_w (h_b - 0.9)/(0.1) (0.004) \text{ m}^2;$$

.1.3 for bulwarks between 1.2 m and 0.9 m in height:

$A_c = 0.00 \text{ m}^2$;

.2 the corrected freeing port area $(A_w = A' + A_c)$ is then adjusted for absence of sheer, if applicable, and height above freeboard deck as in .2.2 and .2.5 above, using h_s and h_w.

.4 The resulting freeing port areas for the open superstructure (A_s) and for the open well (A_w) should be provided along each side of the open space covered by the open superstructure and each side of the open well respectively.

.5 The above relationships should be summarized by the following equations, assuming l_t, the sum of l_w and l_s, is greater than 20 m:

.1 freeing port area A_w for the open well:

$A_w = (0.07 l_w + A_c)$ (sheer correction) $(0.5 h_s/h_w)$; and

.2 freeing port area A_s for the open superstructure:

$A_s = (0.07 l_t)$ (sheer correction) (b_o/l_t) $(l - (l_w/l_t)^2)(0.5 h_s/h_w)$,

Where l_t is 20 m or less, the basic freeing port area is $A = 0.7 + 0.035 l_t$ in accordance with regulation 24(1). Units should be consistent with those in the Convention.

Freeing ports *(regulation 24(1) and (5))*
(IACS interpretation LL.13)

Regulation 24(1)

On a flush deck ship with a substantial deckhouse amidships the deckhouse is considered to provide sufficient break to form two wells and each could be given the required freeing port area based upon the length of the "well". It would not then be necessary to base the area upon 0.7L.

In defining a substantial deckhouse the breadth of the deckhouse should be at least 80% of the beam of the vessel, and the passageways along the side of the ship should not exceed 1.5 m in width.

Where a screen bulkhead is fitted completely across the vessel, at the forward end of a midship deckhouse, this would effectively divide the exposed deck into wells and no limitation on the breadth of the deckhouse is considered necessary in this case.

Wells on raised quarter-decks should be treated as previously, i.e. as being on freeboard decks

Regulation 24(5)

With zero or little sheer on the exposed freeboard deck or an exposed superstructure deck the freeing port area should be spread along the length of the well.

Freeing ports *(regulation 24(3))*
(IACS interpretation LL.44)

The effectiveness of the freeing port area in bulwarks required by regulation 24(1) and (2) depends on free flow across the deck of a ship. Where there is no free flow due to the presence of a continuous trunk or hatchway coaming, the freeing port area in bulwarks is calculated in accordance with regulation 24(3).

The free flow area on deck is the net area of gaps between hatchways, and between hatchways and superstructures and deckhouses up to the actual height of the bulwark.

The freeing port area in bulwarks should be assessed in relation to the net flow area as follows:

.1 If the free flow area is not less than the freeing port area calculated from regulation 24(3) as if the hatchway coamings were continuous, then the minimum freeing port area calculated from regulation 24(1) and (2) should be deemed sufficient.

.2 If the free flow area is equal to, or less than the area calculated from regulation 24(1) and (2), minimum freeing port area in the bulwarks should be determined from regulation 24(3).

.3 If the free flow area is smaller than calculated from regulation 24(3) but greater than calculated from regulation 24(1) and (2), the minimum freeing port area in the bulwark should be determined from the following formula:

$$F = F_1 + F_2 - f_p \ (m^2)$$

where

F_1 is the minimum freeing port area calculated from regulation 24(1) and (2).

F_2 is the minimum freeing port area calculated from regulation 24(3).

f_p is the total net area of passages and gaps between hatch ends and superstructures or deckhouses up to the actual height of bulwark.

See also the interpretations of regulations 24(1) and 24(4) and of regulations 24(1) and (5)

Protection of the crew *(regulation 25(2))*
(IACS interpretation LL.14)

A guard rail should also be required for first tier deckhouses and for superstructures' ends.

Guard rails *(regulation 25(2) and (3))*
(IACS interpretation LL.47/Rev.1)

Fixed, removable or hinged stanchions should be fitted about 1.5 m apart.

At least every third stanchion should be supported by a bracket or stay.

Wire ropes should be accepted in lieu of guard rails in special circumstances and then only in limited lengths.

Lengths of chain should be accepted in lieu of guard rails if they are fitted between two fixed stanchions and/or bulwarks.

The openings between courses should be in accordance with regulation 25(3).

Wires should be made taut by means of turnbuckles.

Removable or hinged stanchions should be capable of being locked in the upright position.

Protection of crew *(regulations 25(4), 26(2) and 27(7) and SOLAS regulation II-1/3-3)*
(IACS interpretation LL.50/Rev.4.1)

1 When applying regulations 25(4), 26(2) and 27(7) of the 1966 LL Convention, as well as SOLAS regulation II-1/3-3, the protection of crew should be provided at least by one of the means denoted in the table given below:

Type of ship	Locations of access in ship	Assigned summer freeboard	Acceptable arrangements according to type of freeboard assigned:			
			Type A	Type B-100	Type B-60	Type B & B+
All ships other than oil tankers*, chemical tanker* and gas carriers*	1.1 Access to midship quarters 1.1.1 Between poop and bridge, or	≤3000 mm	a b e	a b e	a b c(1) e f(1)	
	1.1.2 Between poop and deckhouse containing living accommodation or navigation equipment or both	>3000 mm	a b e	a b e	a b c(1) c(2) e f(1) f(2)	a b c(1) c(2) c(4) d(1) d(2) d(3) e f(1) f(2) f(4)
	1.2 Access to ends 1.2.1 Between poop and bow (if there is no bridge) 1.2.2 Between bridge and bow, or	≤3000 mm	a b c(1) e f(1)	a b c(1) c(2) e f(1) f(2)	a b c(1) c(2) e f(1) f(2)	
	1.2.3 Between a deckhouse containing living accommodation or navigation equipment, or both and bow, or 1.2.4 In the case of a flush deck ship, between crew accommodation and the forward and after ends of ship	>3000 mm	a b c(1) d(1) e f(1)	a b c(1) c(2) d(1) d(2) e f(1) f(2)	a b c(1) c(2) c(4) d(1) d(2) d(3) e f(1) f(2) f(4	

* Oil tankers, chemical tankers and gas carriers as defined in SOLAS regulations II-1/2.12, VII/8.2 and VII/11.2, respectively.

Type of ship	Locations of access in ship	Assigned summer freeboard	Acceptable arrangements according to type of freeboard assigned: Type A
Oil tankers★, chemical tankers★ and gas carriers★	2.1 Access to bow 2.1.1 Between poop and bow or 2.1.2 Between a deckhouse containing living accommodation or navigational equipment, or 2.1.3 In the case of a flush deck ship, between crew accommodation and the forward ends of ship.	$\leqslant (A_f + H_s)^\dagger$	a e f(1) f(5)
		$> (A_f + H_s)^\dagger$	a e f(1) f(2)
	2.2 Access to after end In the case of a flush deck ship, between crew accommodation and the after end of ship		as required in 1.2.4 for other types of ships

★ Oil tankers, chemical tankers and gas carriers as defined in SOLAS regulations II-1/2.12, VII/8.2 and VII/11.2, respectively.

† A_f = the minimum summer freeboard calculated as type 'A' ship regardless of the type freeboard actually assigned.

H_s = the standard height of superstructure as defined in LL regulation 33.

Note: Deviations from some or all of these requirements or alternative arrangements for such cases as ships with very high gangways (i.e. certain gas carriers) may be allowed subject to agreement on a case-by-case basis with the relevant Administration.

2   For oil tankers, as defined in SOLAS regulation II-1/2.12, chemical tankers as defined in SOLAS regulation VII/8.2 or gas carriers as defined in SOLAS regulation VII/11.2, constructed before 1 July 1998, existing arrangements which complied with (b) or (c) may be accepted in lieu of (e) or (f) provided such existing arrangements are fitted with shelters and means of access to and from the deck as required for the arrangements (e) or (f) as defined below.

3   For tankers less than 100 m in length, the minimum width of the gangway platform or deck level walkway fitted in accordance with arrangement (e) or (f), respectively, may be reduced to 0.6 m.

4   Acceptable arrangements referred to in the table are defined as follows:

(a) A well lighted and ventilated under-deck passageway (clear opening 0.8 m wide, 2 m high) as close as practicable to the freeboard deck, connecting and providing access to the locations in question.

(b) A permanent and efficiently constructed gangway fitted at or above the level of the superstructure deck on or as near as practicable to the centreline of the ship, providing a continuous platform, at least 0.6 m in width and a non-slip surface, with guard rails extending on each side throughout its length. Guard rails should be at least 1 m high with courses as required in LL regulation 25(3), and supported by stanchions spaced not more than 1.5 m; a foot-stop should be provided.

(c) A permanent walkway at least 0.6 m in width fitted at freeboard deck level consisting of two rows of guard rails with stanchions spaced not more than 3 m. The number of courses of rails and their spacing should be as required by LL regulation 25(3). On type B ships, hatchway coamings not less than 0.6 m in height may be regarded as forming one side of the walkway, provided that between the hatchways two rows of guard rails are fitted.

(d) A 10 mm minimum diameter wire rope lifeline supported by stanchions about 10 m apart, or a single hand rail or wire rope attached to hatch coamings, continued and adequately supported between hatchways.

(e) A permanent and efficiently constructed gangway fitted at or above the level of the superstructure deck on or as near as practicable to the centreline of the ship:

  – located so as not to hinder easy access across the working areas of the deck;

  – providing a continuous platform at least 1 m in width;

  – constructed of fire-resistant and non-slip material;

  – fitted with guard rails extending on each side throughout its length; guard rails should be at least 1 m high with courses as required by LL regulation 25(3) and supported by stanchions spaced not more than 1.5 m;

  – provided with a foot-stop on each side;

  – having openings, with ladders, where appropriate, to and from the deck. Openings should not be more than 40 m apart;

  – having shelters of substantial construction set in way of the gangway at intervals not exceeding 45 m if the length of the exposed deck to be traversed exceeds 70 m. Every such shelter should be capable of accommodating at least one person and be so constructed as to afford weather protection on the forward, port and starboard sides.

(f) A permanent and efficiently constructed walkway fitted at freeboard deck level on or as near as practicable to the centreline of the ship having the same specifications as those for a permanent gangway listed in (e) except for foot-stops. On type 'B' ships (certified for the carriage of liquids in bulk), with a combined height of hatch coamings and fitted hatch cover of together not less than 1 m in height the hatchway coaming may be regarded as forming one side of the walkway, provided that between the hatchways two rows of guard rails are fitted.

5   Alternative transverse locations for (c), (d) and (f) above, where appropriate:

.1   At or near centreline of ship; or fitted on hatchways at or near centreline of ship.

.2   Fitted on each side of the ship.

.3   Fitted on one side of the ship, provision being made for fitting on either side.

.4   Fitted on one side only.

.5   Fitted on each side of the hatchways as near to the centreline as practicable.

Notes:

1   In all cases where wire ropes are fitted, adequate devices should be provided to ensure their tautness.

2   Wire ropes may only be accepted in lieu of guard rails in special circumstances and then only in limited lengths.

3   Lengths of chain may only be accepted in lieu of guard rails if fitted between two fixed stanchions.

4   Where stanchions are fitted, every third stanchion should be supported by a bracket or stay.

5   Removable or hinged stanchions should be capable of being locked in the upright position.

6   A means of passage over obstructions, if any, such as pipes or other fittings of a permanent nature should be provided.

7   Generally, the width of the gangway or deck-level walkway should not exceed 1.5 m.

Cargo manifold gutter bars – freeing arrangements and intact stability
(regulation 26)
(IACS interpretation LL.59)

Where gutter bars are installed on the weather decks of tankers in way of cargo manifolds and are extended aft as far as the after house front for the purpose of containing cargo spills on deck during loading and discharge operations, the free surface effects caused by containment of a cargo spill during liquid transfer operations or of boarding seas while under way require consideration with respect to the ship's available margin of positive initial stability (GM_o).

Where the gutter bars installed are greater than 300 mm in height, they should be treated as bulwarks according to the Convention with freeing ports arranged in accordance with regulation 24 and effective closures provided for use during loading and discharge operations. Attached closures should be arranged in such a way that jamming cannot occur while at sea, ensuring that the freeing ports will remain fully effective.

On ships without deck camber or where the height of the installed gutter bars exceeds the camber, and for tankers having cargo tanks exceeding 60% of the ship's maximum beam at midships regardless of gutter bar height, gutter bars should not be accepted without an assessment of the initial stability

(GM_o) for compliance with the relevant intact stability requirement taking into account the free surface effects caused by liquids contained by the gutter bars.

See also the interpretations of regulations 17(1), 26(1), 27(9) and 27(10) and of regulations 25(4), 26(2) and 27(7)

Freeing arrangement *(regulations 26(5), 27(7) and 36(1)(e))*
(IACS interpretation LL.23)

Regulations 26(5) and 36(1)(e): *Freeing arrangements for type 'A' ships and type 'B' ships with trunks*

It is considered that a freeing port area, in the lower part of the bulwarks, of 33% of the total area of the bulwarks provides the "other effective freeing arrangements" mentioned in regulation 26(5), and may be considered equivalent to the 50% open rails in way of trunks required by regulation 36(1)(e).

Regulation 27(7): *Freeing arrangements on ships having reduced 'B' freeboard assigned and fitted with bulwarks on the freeboard deck*

For type 'B' ships with freeboards reduced by not more than 60% of the difference between B and A tables there shall be freeing port area in the lower part of the bulwarks equal to at least 25% of the total area of the bulwarks.

The upper edge of the sheer strake shall be kept as low as possible.

See also the interpretations of regulations 16 and 27(7)(c) and of regulations 17(1), 26(1), 27(9) and 27(10)

Freeboard for lighters and barges *(regulation 27(11))*
(IACS interpretation LL.34)

In applying regulation 27(11) to deck cargo barges only a type 'B' freeboard should be assigned, even if the barges possess the same integrity of exposed decks and equivalent safety against flooding as normal tank barges. A type 'A' freeboard can be assigned only to liquid cargo barges. Furthermore deck cargo should be carried only on barges to which type 'B' freeboard is assigned.

Access openings on barges *(regulation 27(11))*
(IACS interpretation LL.42)

In applying regulation 27(11) only those openings which are less than 1.5 m^2 in area should be considered as "small access openings".

Access plates should be considerd as being equivalent to an intact deck on unmanned barges, provided they are secured by closely spaced bolts, are properly gasketted and for all practical purposes have equivalent structural integrity and tightness as an intact deck.

Freeboard tables *(regulation 28)*
(IACS interpretation LL.18)

Freeboards for type 'A' ships with lengths of between 365 m and 400 m should be determined by the following formula:

$$f = 221 + 16.10L - 0.02L^2$$

where f is the freeboard in millimetres

L is the length as defined in regulation 3(1).

Freeboards for type 'A' ships with lengths of 400 m and above should be the constant value, 3460 mm.

Freeboards for type 'B' ships with lengths between 365 m and 400 m should be determined by the following formula:

$$f = -587 + 23L - 0.0188L^2$$

where f is the freeboard in millimetres

L is the length as defined in regulation 3(1).

Freeboards for type 'B' ships with lengths of 400 m and above should be the constant value, 5605 mm.

Trunks *(regulations 29, 31, 35, 36, 37 and 38)*
(IACS interpretation LL.41)

Where the length of a trunk, corrected for breadth and height as may be appropriate, can be included in the effective length used for calculating the correction for superstructures in accordance with regulation 37, it should not be taken into account for calculating the total length (S) for the purpose of sheer correction according to regulation 38(13).

The effective length of superstructures (E) which is used for calculating the freeboard correction according to regulation 29 should be determined excluding the length of trunks.

The inclusion of a trunk in the calculation of freeboard need not prohibit the fitting of openings in the bulkheads of adjacent superstructures such as poops, bridges or forecastles provided there is no direct communication between the superstructure and the trunk.

The sides of a trunk included in the calculation of freeboard should be intact. Sidescuttles of the non-opening type and bolted manhole covers may be allowed.

Negative depth correction *(regulation 31(3))*
(IACS interpretation LL.24)

When the height of a superstructure, raised quarter-deck or trunk is less than the corresponding standard height, the calculated reduction should be corrected in the ratio of the height of the actual superstructure, raised quarter-deck or trunk, to the applicable standard height as defined in regulation 33.

Length of superstructure *(regulation 34)*
(IACS interpretation LL.15)

Regulation 34(1)

Where a superstructure bulkhead is recessed, the effective length of the superstructure should be reduced by an amount equivalent in area to the area of the recess related to the breadth of the ship at the mid-length of the recess.

Where the recess is unsymmetrical about the centreline, the largest portion of the recess should be considered as applying to both sides of the ship.

Such a recess need not be decked over.

Regulation 34(2)

Where there is an extension to a superstructure, which extension has a breadth on each side of the centreline of at least 30% of the breadth of the ship, the effective length of the superstructure may be increased by considering an equivalent superstructure bulkhead in the form of a parabola. This parabola should extend from the extension at the centreline and pass through the junction of the actual superstructure bulkhead with the sides of the extension and extend to the sides of the ship. This parabola should be completely contained within the boundary of the superstructure and its extensions.

Treatment of superstructures with sloping end bulkheads
(regulations 34, 35 and 38(12))
(IACS interpretation LL.37/Rev.1)

When taking account of superstructures which have sloping end bulkheads, in the calculations of freeboards, such superstructures should be dealt with in the following manner:

Length of superstructure (regulation 34)

1   When the height of superstructure, clear of the slope, is equal to or smaller than the standard height, the length (S) should be obtained as shown in figure 4.

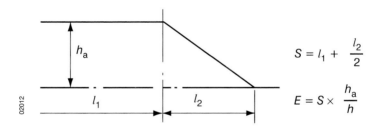

$$S = l_1 + \frac{l_2}{2}$$

$$E = S \times \frac{h_a}{h}$$

Figure 4 – *Height of superstructure equal to or smaller than the standard height (h)*

2   When the height is greater than the standard, the length (S) should be obtained as shown in figure 5.

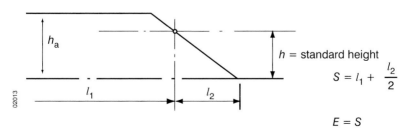

h = standard height

$$S = l_1 + \frac{l_2}{2}$$

$$E = S$$

Figure 5 – *Height of superstructure greater than the standard height*

223

3   The foregoing should apply only when the slope, related to the base line, is 15° or greater. Where the slope is less than 15°, the configuration should be treated as sheer.

Effective length of superstructure (regulation 35)

When the height of the superstructure, clear of the slope, is less than the standard height, its effective length (*E*) should be its length (*S*) as obtained from paragraph 1 above, reduced in the ratio of its actual height to the standard height.

Sheer (regulation 38(12))

When a poop or a forecastle has sloping end bulkheads, and sheer credit may be allowed on account of excess height, the formula given in regulation 38(12) should be used, the values of *y* and *L'* being as shown in figure 6.

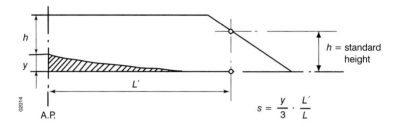

Figure 6 – *Sheer credit (s) for excess height*

See also the interpretation of regulations 29, 31, 35, 36, 37 and 38

Effective length of superstructure *(regulation 35(3) and (4))*

With particular regard to the length of raised quarter-deck in paragraphs (3) and (4) of this regulation, the following interpretation applies:

> In a ship with a superstructure which extends over the whole length of the freeboard deck, the part of the superstructure from the after perpendicular up to a maximum of 0.6*L* may be treated as a raised quarter-deck. In this respect, if no watertight front bulkhead is fitted the bow may be considered to act as such.

> The length limit imposed by paragraph (4) of this regulation for a raised quarter-deck of less than standard height applies to the length calculated as indicated in paragraph (3) of this regulation.

Effective length of raised quarter-deck *(regulation 35(4))*
(IACS interpretation LL.25)

The maximum effective length of 0.6*L* of a raised quarter-deck which is stipulated by regulation 35(4), should be measured from the after perpendicular even where a poop is fitted in conjunction with the raised quarter-deck.

Continuous hatchways as trunk *(regulation 36)*
(IACS interpretation LL.26/Rev.1)

It is recommended that continuous hatchways may be treated as a trunk in the freeboard computation provided regulation 36 is complied with in all respects.

The trunk deck stringer referred to in regulation 36(1)(b) may be fitted outboard of the trunk side bulkhead in association with the following:

.1 The stringer so formed is to provide a clear walkway of at least 450 mm in width on each side of the ship.

.2 The stringer is to be of solid plate efficiently supported and stiffened.

.3 The stringer is to be as high above the freeboard deck as practicable. In the freeboard calculation, the trunk height is to be reduced by at least 600 mm or by the actual difference between the top of the trunk and the stringer, whichever is greater.

.4 Hatch cover securing appliances are to be accessible from the stringer or walkway.

.5 The breadth of the trunk is to be measured between the trunk side bulkheads.

.6 Regulation 36 is to be complied with in all other respects.

See also the interpretation of regulations 26(5), 27(7) and 36(1)(e)

Less than standard height hatch coamings on trunks of less than standard height *(regulation 36(4))*
(IACS interpretation LL.27)

In the case where the trunk height is less than standard and the trunk hatch coamings are also of less than standard height, or omitted entirely, doubt may arise whether the trunk hatchways are located in position 1 or position 2 and, consequently, about the reduction to be made in the actual trunk height. In these cases the reduction from the actual height of trunk on account of insufficient hatch coaming height should be taken as the difference between 600 mm and the actual height of coaming, or 600 mm if no hatch coamings are fitted. Reduction in the actual height of trunk should not be required in cases where only small hatches with less than standard height are fitted in the trunk deck for which dispensation from the requirement of standard coaming height may be given.

Deduction for superstructures and trunks *(regulation 37)*
(IACS interpretation LL.28)

For the purpose of applying the table "Percentage of deduction for type 'B' ships" in regulation 37(2) it is considered that any detached superstructure abaft midship whose after bulkhead is located $0.05L$ or more forward of the after perpendicular may be treated as a detached bridge.

A superstructure whose after bulkhead is located within $0.05L$ from the after perpendicular should not qualify as a detached bridge.

Any excess in the height of such a superstructure, which does not extend to the after perpendicular, cannot be regarded as contributing to the sheer allowance contemplated in regulation 38(12).

Sheer credit for superimposed superstructures
(regulations 38(5), 38(7) and 38(12))
(IACS interpretation LL.29/Rev.1)

Superstructures superimposed on a complete superstructure (regulation 38(5))

In applying regulation 38(5) (sheer on a complete superstructure ship) where there is an enclosed poop or forecastle superimposed on a complete superstructure, sheer credit should be allowed for such a poop or forecastle, according to the method of regulation 38(12) as shown in figure 7.

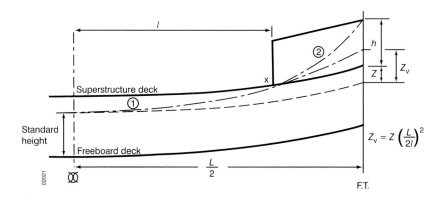

Figure 7

Superstructures superimposed on a forecastle or poop (i.e. a stepped forecastle or poop) (regulation 38(7))

In applying regulation 38(7) and 38(12) where a poop or forecastle consists of two layers, the method shown in figure 8 should be used.

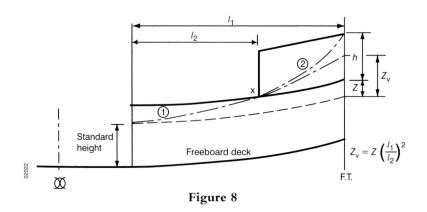

Figure 8

226

In the above the following definitions should apply:

Z is as defined in regulation 38(5)

Z_v is the end ordinate of a virtual standard parabolic curve taken through the point "x". If Z_v is greater than $(Z + h)$, the end ordinate should be $(Z + h)$, in which case point "x" should be disregarded and curve ② not taken into account.

When the length of the first tier superstructure is greater than $0.5L$, the virtual standard parabolic curve should commence at amidships as indicated in figure 7.

Sheer allowance for excess height of superstructure
(regulation 38(7) and (12))
(IACS interpretation LL.30)

As regulation 38(7) and (12) does not refer to a raised quarter-deck, credit should be given for this type of superstructure only where the height of the raised quarter-deck is greater than the standard height of "other super-structures" as defined in regulation 33, and only for the amount by which the actual height of the raised quarter-deck exceeds that standard height.

Sheer *(regulation 38(12))*
(IACS interpretation LL.16)

Where the height of a superstructure is less than standard, paragraph 12 may be applied, except that the superstructure deck should be not less than the minimum height of the superstructure above the virtual sheer curve at any point.

For this purpose "y" should be taken as the difference between the actual and minimum height of the superstructure at the end of sheer.

Sheer *(regulation 38(12))*

The final explanatory subparagraph of paragraph (12) of regulation 38 should be interpreted to read:

"The above formula determines the mean ordinate of a curve in the form of a parabola tangent to the actual sheer curve of the freeboard deck at the after end of a forecastle or at the forward end of a poop, and intersecting the end ordinate at a point below the superstructure deck a distance equal to the standard height of a superstructure. The superstructure deck should not be less than standard height above this curve at any point. This curve should be used in determining the sheer profile for forward and after halves of the ship."

See also the interpretation of regulations 34, 35 and 38(12)

Deduction for excess sheer *(regulation 38(15))*
(IACS interpretation LL.31)

Since no stipulation is made as to the height of the superstructure referred to in regulation 38(15), the height of this superstructure should be related to its standard height. When the height of the superstructure or raised quarter-deck is less than standard, the reduction should be in the ratio of the actual to the standard height thereof.

Bow height *(regulation 39(2))*
(IACS interpretation LL.38/Rev.1)

1   When calculating the bow height, the sheer of the forecastle deck may be taken into account, even if the length of the forecastle is less than $0.15L$, but greater than $0.07L$, provided that the forecastle height is not less than one half of standard height of superstructure as defined in regulation 33 between $0.07L$ and the forward terminal.

2   Where the forecastle height is less than one half of standard height of superstructure, as defined in regulation 33, the credit bow height may be determined as follows:

.1   when the freeboard deck has sheer extending from abaft $0.15L$, by a parabolic curve having its origin at $0.15L$ abaft the forward terminal at a height equal to the midship depth of the ship, extended through the point of intersection of forecastle bulkhead and deck, and up to a point at the forward terminal not higher than the level of the forecastle deck. However, if the value of the height denoted h_t in figure 9 is smaller than the value of the height denoted h_b, then h_t may be replaced by h_b in the available bow height (figure 9).

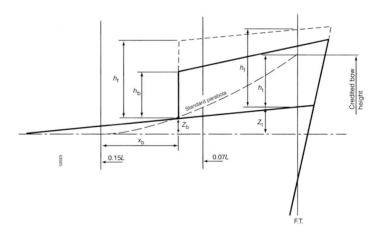

Figure 9

h_t = Half standard height of superstructure as defined in regulation 33

$$h_t = Z_b \frac{(0.15L)^2}{X_b} - Z_t$$

.2   when the freeboard deck has sheer extending for less than $0.15L$ or has no sheer, by a line from the forecastle deck at side at $0.07L$ extended parallel to the base line to the forward terminal (figure 10).

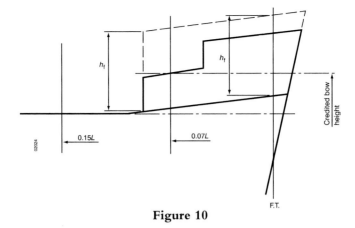

Figure 10

Minimum bow height *(regulation 39)*
(IACS interpretation LL.43)

When applying regulation 39 to ships which have been assigned timber freeboards the bow height should be measured from the summer load waterline and not from the timber summer load waterline.

Minimum freeboards *(regulation 40)*

When the geometric freeboard calculated in accordance with paragaph (1) is less than the minimum freeboard allowed by paragraph (2) of this regulation, the corrections for winter freeboard and Winter North Atlantic freeboard should be added to the allowed minimum summer freeboard and not to the calculated value. Similarly, the allowance for fresh water should be a deduction from the allowed minimum freeboard.

See also the interpretation of regulations 3(5)(c) and (9) and 40(1)

Stowage *(regulation 44)*

The following text should be regarded as an interpretation of regulation 44 in order to harmonize this regulation with the Code of Safe Practice for Ships Carrying Timber Deck Cargoes (resolution A.287(VIII)).

Stowage

General

Openings in the weather deck over which cargo is stowed should be securely closed and battened down.

The ventilators and air pipes should be efficiently protected.

Timber deck cargoes should extend over at least the entire available length which is the total length of the well or wells between superstructures.

Where there is no limiting superstructure at the after end, the timber should extend at least to the after end of the aftermost hatchway.

The timber deck cargo should extend athwartships as close as possible to the ship side due allowance being given for obstructions such as guard rails bulwark stays, uprights, etc. provided any gap thus created at the side of the ship does not exceed 4% of the breadth (*b*). The timber should be stowed as solidly as possible to at least the standard height of a superstructure other than a raised quarter-deck.

On a ship within a seasonal winter zone in winter, the height of the deck cargo above the weather deck should not exceed one-third of the extreme breadth of the ship.

The timber deck cargo should be compactly stowed, lashed and secured. It should not interfere in any way with the navigation and necessary work of the ship.

Uprights

Uprights, when required by the nature of the timber, should be of adequate strength considering the breadth of the ship; the strength of the uprights should not exceed the strength of the bulwark and the spacing should be suitable for the length and character of timber carried, but should not exceed 3 m. Strong angles or metal sockets or equally efficient means should be provided for securing the uprights.

Lashings

Timber deck cargo should be efficiently secured throughout its length by independent overall lashings.

The spacing of the lashings should be determined by the maximum height of the cargo above the weather deck in the vicinity of the lashing:

> .1 for a height of 4 m and below the spacing should be not more than 3 m;
>
> .2 for a height of 6 m and above the spacing should be not more than 1.5 m;
>
> .3 at intermediate heights the average spacing should be obtained by linear interpolation.

Where the height of timber deck cargo exceeds 6 m the strength of the lashings should be to the satisfaction of the Administration.

Eye plates for these lashings should be efficiently attached to the sheer strake or to the deck stringer plate. The distance from an end bulkhead of a superstructure to the first eye plate should be not more than 2 m. Eye plates and lashings should be provided 0.6 m and 1.5 m from the ends of timber deck cargoes where there is no bulkhead.

The lashings should be capable of withstanding an ultimate load of not less than 13,600 kg. They should be fitted with sliphooks and turnbuckles, which should be accessible at all times.

Wire rope lashings should have a short length of long link chain to permit the length of lashings to be regulated.

When timber is in lengths of less than 3.6 m, the spacing of the lashings should be reduced or other suitable provisions made to suit the length of timber.

Shackles, stretching devices and all other ancillary components incorporated into a chain or wire rope lashing and its securings should have a minimum ultimate load of 14,100 kg. Each component should be proof loaded to 5,600 kg. No part should be damaged or permanently deformed after proof loading.

Stability

Provision should be made for a safe margin of stability at all stages of the voyage, regard being given to additions of weight, such as those due to absorption of water and icing and to losses of weight such as those due to consumption of fuel and stores.

Protection of crew, access to machinery spaces, etc.

In addition to the requirements of regulation 25(5), guard rails or lifelines not more than 330 mm apart vertically should be provided on each side of the cargo deck to a height of at least 1 m above the cargo.

In addition a lifeline, preferably wire rope, set up taut with a stretching screw, should be provided as near as practicable to the centreline of the ship. The stanchion supports to all guard rails and lifelines should be spaced so as to prevent undue sagging. Where the cargo is uneven, a safe walking surface of not less than 600 mm in width should be fitted over the cargo and effectively secured beneath or adjacent to the lifeline.

Steering arrangements

Steering arrangements should be effectively protected from damage by cargo and, as far as practicable, should be accessible. Efficient provision should be made for steering in the event of a breakdown in the main steering arrangements.

Timber freeboards for ships having reduced type 'B' freeboards assigned (regulation 45(2) and (3))
(IACS interpretation LL.33)

Some Administrations accept that timber freeboards may be assigned to ships with reduced type 'B' freeboards, provided the timber freeboards are calculated on the basis of the ordinary type 'B' freeboard.

Regulation 45(2) and (3) should be interpreted such that the Timber Winter mark and/or the Timber Winter North Atlantic mark are placed at the same level as the reduced type 'B' Winter mark when the computed Timber Winter mark and/or the computed Timber Winter North Atlantic mark fall below the reduced type 'B' Winter mark.

Part 6
Form of record of conditions of assignment of load lines

INTERNATIONAL CONVENTION ON LOAD LINES, 1966

RECORD OF CONDITIONS OF ASSIGNMENT

Name of ship . . . .

Port of registry . . . .

Nationality . . . .

Distinctive number or letters . . . .

Shipbuilders . . . .

Yard number . . . .

Date of construction/conversion . . . .

Freeboard assigned as a ship of Type . . . .

Classification. . . . .

Date and place of initial survey . . . .

A plan of suitable size may be attached to this Report in preference to sketches on this page.

Disposition and dimensions of superstructures, trunks, deckhouses, machinery casings; extent of bulwarks, guard rails and wood sheathing on exposed deck, to be inserted in the diagrams and tables following; together with positions of hatchways, gangways and other means for the protection of the crew; cargo ports, bow and stern doors, sidescuttles, scuppers, ventilators, air pipes, companionways, and other items that would affect the seaworthiness of the ship.

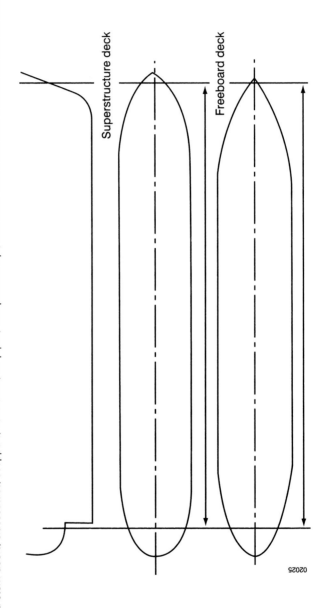

Superstructure deck

Freeboard deck

02025

Doorways in superstructures, exposed machinery casings and deckhouses protecting openings in freeboard and superstructure decks (Regulations 12, 17 and 18)

Location	Ref. No. on sketch or plan	Number and size of openings	Height of sills	Closing appliances	
				Type and material	Number of clips
In forecastle bulkhead					
In bridge forward bulkhead					
In bridge after bulkhead					
In raised quarter-deck bulkhead					
In poop bulkhead					
In exposed machinery casings on freeboard or raised quarter-decks					

Doorways in superstructures, exposed machinery casings and deckhouses protecting openings in freeboard and superstructure decks *(continued)*

Location	Ref. No. on sketch or plan	Number and size of openings	Height of sills	Closing appliances	
				Type and material	Number of clips
In exposed machinery casings on superstructure decks					
In machinery casings within super-structures or deckhouses on freeboard deck					
In deckhouses in Position 1 enclosing openings leading below freeboard deck					
In deckhouses in Position 2 enclosing openings leading within enclosed super-structures or below freeboard deck					
In exposed pump-room casings					

Hatchways at positions 1 and 2 closed by portable covers and secured weathertight by tarpaulins and battening devices (Regulation 15)

Position and Reference No. on sketch or plan						
Dimensions of clear opening at top of coaming						
Height of coamings above deck						
PORTABLE BEAMS — Number						
Spacing						
$b_1 \times t_f$						
$D \times t_w$						
$b_2 \times t_f$						
Bearing surface						
Means of securing each beam						
PORTABLE COVERS — Material						
Thickness						
Direction fitted						
Bearing surface						
Spacing of cleats						
TARPAULINS — No. of layers						
Material						

Means of securing each section of covers:

Are wood covers fitted with galvanized end bands?

239

Hatchways at positions 1 and 2 closed by weathertight covers of steel (or other equivalent material) fitted with gaskets and clamping devices (Regulation 16)

Position and Reference No. on sketch or plan	Dimensions of clear opening at top of coaming	Height of coamings above deck	Type of cover or patent name	Material

Machinery space openings and miscellaneous openings in freeboard and superstructure decks (Regulations 17 and 18)

Positions and Reference No. on sketch or plan								
Dimensions								
Height of coaming								
COVER { Material								
COVER { How attached								
Number and spacing of toggles								
Position and Reference No. on sketch or plan								
Dimensions								
Height of coaming								
COVER { Material								
COVER { How attached								
Number and spacing of toggles								

Ventilators on freeboard and superstructure decks (positions 1 and 2) (Regulation 19)

Deck on which fitted	Number fitted	Coaming		Type (State patent name if any)	Closing appliances
		Dimensions	Height		

Air pipes on freeboard and superstructure decks (Regulation 20)

Deck on which fitted	Number fitted	Coaming		Type (State patent name if any)	Closing appliances
		Dimensions	Height		

Cargo port and other similar openings (Regulation 21)

Position of port	Dimensions of opening	Distance of lower edge from freeboard deck	Securing devices	Remarks

Scuppers, inlets and discharges (Regulation 22)

State if scupper or discharge	Number	Pipe			From	Vertical distance above top of keel			Number, type and material of discharge valves	Position of controls
		Diameter	Thickness	Material		Discharge		Uppermost valve		
						Outlet in hull	Inboard end			

S – Scupper
D – Discharge

MS – Mild steel
CS – Cast steel
GM – Gun metal
Any other approved material to be designated

SD   – Screw-down
ANR   – Automatic non-return
SD ANR – Screw-down automatic non-return

Sidescuttles (Regulation 23)

| Position | Number fitted | Clear glass size | Fixed or opening | Material | | Type of glass and thickness | Standards used and Type No. |
				Frame	Deadlight		

Indicate the vertical distance between the freeboard deck and the lower sill of the sidescuttle positioned at the greatest vertical distance below the freeboard deck.

246

Freeing ports (Regulation 24)

	Length of bulwark	Height of bulwark	Number and size of freeing ports each side	Total area each side	Required area each side
Freeboard deck after well					
Forward well					
Superstructure deck					

State fore and aft position of each freeing port in relation to superstructure end bulkheads { After well Forward well

Particulars of shutters, bars or rails fitted to freeing ports

Height of lower edge of freeing port above deck

Protection of the crew (Regulations 25 and 26)

State particulars of bulwarks or guard rails on freeboard and superstructure decks:

State details of lifelines, walkways, gangways or underdeck passageways where required to be fitted:

Timber deck cargo fittings (Regulation 44)

State particulars of uprights, sockets, lashings, guard rails and lifelines:

Other special features

The conditions of assignment shown on this form are a record of the arrangements and fittings provided on the ship and are in accordance with the requirements of the relevant regulations of the International Convention on Load Lines, 1966.

. . . .
(Surveyor's signature)

. . . .
(Date)